TALES OF ASTERRA

Dear Rana,

I hope you enjoy your journey through Asterra! Wishing you many wondrous journeys & adventures!

Best Wishes,

TALES of ASTERRA

MICHAEL FRANK RIZZO

ILLUSTRATED BY ALEJANDRO COLUCCI

LUMINARE PRESS

WWW.LUMINAREPRESS.COM

Printed in the United States of America

Luminare Press
442 Charnelton St.
Eugene, OR 97401
www.luminarepress.com

LCCN: 2022919372
ISBN: 978-1-64388-213-0

For my family, friends, and dogs.
I never would have gathered the courage to write
these stories without your constant love and support.
For Emily, Holly, Keisha, Daisy, Isabella, Angel,
Sophia, Gia, Ella, and Annie—my inspiration.

TABLE OF CONTENTS

Author's Note

Asterra has been a world that I have been creating for almost seven years and was born out of my love for fantasy, mythology, history, and adventure. Most importantly, it was my need for a safe haven when my days seemed too difficult that sparked the initial journey to Asterra. It is a project that is dear to my heart, and one that I am delighted to share with you. The bibliography at the end is a list of sources that served as a source of knowledge and a basis of inspiration for crafting my world. Here, you will find some of my favorite fantasy novels, mythological tales, historical sources, academic materials, dictionaries, and much more. I hope these materials will serve and inspire you in whatever journey you choose in life. And I hope Asterra brings you just as much joy as it brings me.

Kind regards,
Michael Frank Rizzo

PREFACE

Hello there, fellow adventurer. Welcome to the start of your magical journey through the majestical land of Asterra. I am, most humbly, your storytelling guide and tale collector, Penniforth Rodgers, but everyone calls me Penny for short. Now, you might be asking yourself, what does this guy with the odd name and spiffy clothes know about adventures and storytelling?

Well, when I was a young boy growing up in the realm of Caris, an old local merchant had grown quite fond of traveling into my village of Rectitude every week. He set up his wares, which he procured from trading throughout Asterra, in the town square, and it never took him long to grab the attention of all the townsfolk. The other children and their parents were always amazed by his eclectic goods, but to me these paled in comparison to the stories he shared: knights' deeds, pirate curses, fairy parties, and dragons' treasure, all out there somewhere in Asterra—a place that seemed incredibly distant to me in Rectitude.

As a boy, I was nervous and shy, and every road that wasn't my own seemed closed off to me. But each tale the merchant told gave me strength to explore that which I didn't know. In time, I soon found that I was living within just such a magical reality all along, and the majesty of this life was there for me to take whenever I was ready to start my own story. So I promised myself that when I was old enough, I would travel throughout this magnificent land, collecting and documenting the grand stories of Asterra just like the old merchant.

I put faith in my feet and courage in my mind, and I have since spent my years exploring Asterra. Each adventure I embark on leads to a new discovery, a new face, and a new tale. I have met some of my best friends out there on the road yonder. And I receive mail from all over Asterra. That is a lot of postage. As you may or may not know,

Asterra contains well over fifty realms, each of which boasts its own unique culture, traditions, languages, currency, and of course, tales.

In these stories, you will explore and witness many of these differences for yourself. You will see realms in the past that feel more current to our present year of 4124 A.L.Y.; other realms, though their tales are not far removed from the present, have been simply lost somewhere far in the past. Yet all realms harken back to a period before our record of time started: the Lost Years. Every year since then has been marked as A.L.Y., or "After the Lost Years." This naming convention is a monument to the shrouded mystery of our distant past. And the curiosity to discover what came before our records is the catalyst that sparked Asterra's unique and vibrant cultures—forged together and torn asunder by differences known only in truth to time. There are 4,124 years to cover, so there is much to learn, my friend. And our journey shall start with the oldest tale in the collection, nestled deep within the dunes of the great desert realm of Xirtis. From there we shall explore magical forests, quaint seaside towns, and dreadful dungeons together.

You will find that this diverse continent is home to elves, fairies, dwarves, varenijar, esterelians, q'zardi, humans, and many more. The flora and fauna are rich and diverse. Plants rare to the eyes add wonder to every venture, such as the royal regjar root with its regal and medicinal qualities, its beauty contrasted by the peril the ever-watchful ice trolls provide, who often passionately guard it, believing it sacred to their lands.

Some may say that I have made quite the name for myself. Whether this has been for good or bad I do not know. But my goal through these stories is for you to see that there is a tale out there for everyone: that no story is insignificant and no step too small. Unexpected turns and paths can lead us to where we ought to be and discover where we should dare not venture. And at journey's end, know we are better and braver, now that we have left our mark on the road ahead. Go make a name for yourself in this wonderful land—that is, if you haven't already. Never forget that the magic of this reality is here for you to grasp. Within this book, I have compiled fourteen unique tales and one special poem, which come from different times and different areas throughout Asterra.

In my retellings, I have kept true to the tales' original sources while also adding a bit of my own creativity throughout each story in hopes of letting the splendor of Asterra's people shine through brighter than ever. I shall guide you, when need be, but I will let the narrative of each tale draw you in and make my voice known only when truly needed. I have also compiled a glossary of terms, places, flora, fauna, and important figures to enrich your travels. And with the special help of one of my magical friends, I have also created an appendix to summarize the four fundamentals of magic.

I hope you enjoy the journey, and I wish you all the wonders of this life. May you step forth to create and share your own magical tales. You have already made one friend on this path, and I shall be there with you till the end of this journey and hopefully for many more journeys to follow.

Your friend, truly,
Penniforth Octavius Rodgers

Captured Time

L ong ago, among the dunes of the great Altris Desert, there stood a small town called Zeris, which contained a great clock tower unlike any other. Its chimes were the sweetest of sounds, its face more pristine than any crystal, and its accuracy impeccable. At 134 meters tall, the Cammas Clock Tower was the tallest building in Zeris and could be seen for miles out into the Altris. Its time was dictated by a pendulum, which was large enough to batter down the walls of the greatest castles in all the land, and its master was a small man, nearing a century old, who built many clocks of his own.

He was a happy fellow, never taking much for granted or wanting more for fame. All he treasured was time, and he felt he was its keeper—and was that so wrong to believe? Haza Izmir had more clocks than anyone else: mechanical clocks, water clocks, pendulum clocks, cuckoo clocks, grandfather clocks, and many other wondrous clocks powered by some of the most fascinating mechanisms. He knew how each one worked, and he knew just how to repair them. If time stopped for one clock, he would fix it, and he would fix it so well that the clock would be more pristine, and its chimes sweeter, than ever before. For he loved each of them so, and not even the setting sun could take away a fraction of glory from their sight. He preserved them, and in such stewardship, he felt himself preserved and protected from the sands of the desert.

One solemn twilight, a desert wind blew to the east, and old Mr. Izmir could hear the gales from atop his tower as he looked down at the elegant colors of the town bazaar, which brought crowds of people from all over Asterra. Various stands, colored with variegated cloths,

sold marvelous goods, giving birth to mirth and whimsical wonder. The setting desert sun played games, painting tapestries in the far away dunes. Amethyst and amaranthine dreams gleamed in perennial glory, reflecting off the water of Al' Fer's Bay, as the oil lamps and candle lanterns of the town were lit and the city life continued in the illuminated darkness.

As was customary, when the time was just right, Mr. Izmir left his tower to travel into Zeris. He carefully packed up his little cart with his clocks, this process taking longer with each passing year. His back ached and arched more as he aged, so that he could feel the whiskers of his thick gray beard brush against his vestments now. Yet a small sigh was all that he indulged, looking around after the job was done but having no one to greet. He walked through the streets until he found a nice spot to sit and set up his wares. The clocks he displayed served as a testament to his capabilities as a repairer of fine timepieces, and for his services he charged a small, manageable fee. He was the only person within Zeris who was skilled enough to repair the most complex of timepieces, and almost every denizen of the desert knew this to be true.

When the clocks chimed, the lines formed, and Mr. Izmir began his repairs. As was usual, many folks came by his stand and offered great treasures for his clocks on display, but Mr. Izmir could not dare part with a single one of his timepieces. They were his: a collection of memories that eloquently transposed something of his life into a form he could readily see, and they were as true as the stars in the night sky, which told grand journeys of yore.

Mr. Izmir could remember his first clock, and the day and time he had received it. It was a sunny afternoon, and he was overlooking the beautifully serene water of Al' Fer's Bay. His father, a local fisherman, had just returned from sea, and young Haza's mother greeted him with happy tears in her eyes. Haza, as was often the case, had lost track of time waiting to be reunited with his father. His father's solution was a small clock, presented to Haza so that he could never lose the day and time when his father was promised to return.

Haza captured every moment with his new clock, rejoicing when it was time for his father to return. Alas, there came a time when Haza waited and his father never made it back from the sea—an accident had stolen his father's time and his own. Haza's mother was devastated, and her health began to decline over the passing months. Soon all Haza had left was his clock, and the time it so graciously gave to him. He yearned not for friendship nor companionship. His time was his and not worth giving to anyone else. Casting himself away from the world, he found solace only in that which captured time and the old Cammas Clock Tower—that old, abandoned building became his new home, his workshop, and his only friend.

Mr. Izmir focused back on his repairs and continued till late into the evening. When his job was done, he carefully packed his clocks into his cart and began the journey back to his clock tower, walking through the streets and gazing into the Altris and the starry sky above, thinking a light would fain shine upon him as another day drew nearer to its end. Sadly, he had enough time captured in his tower, but it didn't serve him as well as he served it now. He was alone, dragging his mementos of memories into the dark night.

Yet he was here in Zeris to carry on and preserve that which he knew and loved, and he thought that this surely had to be a blessing. With the money he had made, he would buy a plethora of spare parts from traveling vendors who came to Zeris to sell their wares.

With these parts he constructed more clocks and improved upon his existing ones. When his clocks rang, birds congregated near his tower and sang songs of their own, and as his collection grew more marvelous, the sound of the chimes during each hour grew as well, filling the town with beautiful music. However, as each day passed and the music grew ever louder, the individual voice of each timepiece began to fade.

One night he left the bazaar after his job was done, and on his way back home, he found a small clock broken asunder in a lonely, dark alleyway, ready to be lost to the sands. *It was not meant for it to be this way*, he thought. *What cruelty and injustice for the world to cast it aside.* He took the timepiece with him to his tower, for there, in the quiet recesses of his timeless workshop, he would fix it and give it the attention it deserved.

Michael Frank Rizzo

He worked tirelessly and built it anew, allowing the clock to regain its former glory, while also improving the precision of its internal gears and the sweet sound of its chimes. The small clock presented itself before him then as a wondrous new timepiece, and it now had a great many tales to tell. He added it along with the others, and when noontime came, it and its kin sounded their bells and whistles for all the town to hear. They told their tale and let their voices be heard. It was the most beautiful music, and Mr. Izmir tried to hum along, but the clocks were too many and far too loud—his voice was lost somewhere in their sound.

He retreated into the inner workings of the tower, where morose amber chambers housed a peering pathos of time past. Here, Mr. Izmir sat to record his memories, jotting down every last one of them. "A master holds the key to every piece of practice and every moment produced from its magic. For clocks, it is doubly so! What nobler pursuit than to be a purveyor of past and practitioner of future. If the virtuoso hones his craft and creates as he deems just, I surely have done the same." He put his head down in a bout of confusion. *I surely have done the same.*

Alas, the master who is never pleased keeps himself only as a slave to his own pursuit. Mr. Izmir always knew himself to be a preoccupied soul, shifting to sate his heart and mind. And time, of which he was its steward, passed him by. He had no family, no wife, no son, and no friends; all the master had was his clocks that ticked away at the time he had so graciously given them.

Just as every day prior, Mr. Izmir awoke early the next morning to the sound of his clocks, but the sound was much louder to his conscious mind than ever before. When noontime came, the mighty Cammas Clock Tower's bells rang, and Mr. Izmir went into Zeris to set up his stand to repair clocks. As usual, he brought with him a few of his clocks and displayed them for all to see. The customers asked their usual questions and brought forth many wondrous treasures, and he declined them all as he continued with his repairs. Children ran through the crowds, only momentarily looking at Mr. Izmir's work—they had little use in telling time. However, one of the children stopped to look at the clocks and was mesmerized by their beauty. The boy stood there for most of the day until the crowds dissipated and only himself, Mr. Izmir, and a few pedestrians were left.

"Are you the man in the old clock tower?" the boy asked, gazing upon Mr. Izmir's face.

"Yes, I am Haza Izmir, the man who lives in the Cammas Clock Tower. Do you have a clock to be repaired?"

"No, I sadly have none, but I have heard your clocks ring many times, and my bird has traveled to your tower to hear the symphony of your chimes. May I buy one of your clocks for myself and my bird?" the boy said.

"I am afraid to say that these clocks here are not meant to be sold, my friend. Besides, a young boy like you should not be so concerned with timepieces," Mr. Izmir said. "Clocks are relics of time, and they are best kept pristine by other relics like myself."

The boy was not so easily dissuaded though. "How about one of the clocks in your tower? I know that you have many clocks there, and I promise I will take care of whatever piece you allow me to buy."

"I am sorry, but these clocks mean too much to me to sell," Mr. Izmir returned.

The boy left, filled with sadness, and Mr. Izmir felt bad, but he couldn't sell his prized possessions. The following day, the bells and clocks of the tower began to ring again, and Mr. Izmir sat and stared into the desert as the sounds drowned out his own voice. What once was a beautiful melody had become a cacophony of sound, far too loud to be dissected by even the most trained ear, and few birds came to greet Mr. Izmir at the top of his tower.

As his collection continued to grow, Mr. Izmir could not sleep, but all of this seemed necessary for the master of time. Alas, the sound soon left little room for him to think, and the many memories that he was fond of thinking about now also became drowned in noise.

A few weeks passed, and when he walked through the streets of Zeris again, he saw the same young boy from weeks prior and noticed a familiar look of sadness upon the boy's face. "Could I have been the cause of such pain?" Mr. Izmir said to himself as he approached the boy to see what was the matter. "My young friend what causes you such sadness?" he said.

"My bird has flown away, and I have gone throughout all of Zeris calling her name, but I can't seem to find her."

As tears fell from the boy's eyes, Mr. Izmir felt a great pain in his own heart: something released deep inside of him, and he wished not to see the boy endure such sorrow any longer. He thought for a moment and conjured a splendid idea that was sure to work. He left for his tower and returned about an hour later with his cart, which was completely filled with cuckoo clocks. "My clocks have grown so loud as of late that I believe your bird has hidden in fear of the noise. But these clocks are sweet and few, and just maybe your bird will hear the sound of my own birds and return to listen to their music." The boy smiled as Mr. Izmir set up his clocks throughout the streets of Zeris and let the chimes ring.

Within the hour, the boy's bird returned to listen to the mechanical birds sing their tune and sang along. The boy was happy and cried great tears of joy. "You have brought my happiness back. I thank you for your kindness!"

Mr. Izmir was moved when he saw what greatness his clocks could do and what happiness they could impart. To have them sit in his tower and create boisterous sounds in unison only hampered their individual glory.

Mr. Izmir felt a certain relief and peace in this moment, and he turned to the boy and presented him with the greatest cuckoo clock in the collection. "I want you to have this, my good friend. It is a monument to my memories, and I think it is ready to create more memories with a new master."

The boy smiled. "I thank you, Mr. Izmir! I will let it sing every day!" The two said their farewells and parted ways with great happiness.

From this day forward, Mr. Izmir decided to give away a good portion of his clocks, and each and every day he brought his wares into town to sell. The townsfolk were happy, and they bought his clocks until the whole town of Zeris was filled with the sweet music of chimes.

From the solitude of his clock tower, Mr. Izmir observed this spectacle from time to time and was happy, and a glorious moment presented itself each day when he looked upon the bazaar and heard the chimes at noon; across the desert, from the shoals of Al' Fer's Bay to the mightiest of dunes, the song rang loud for all to hear. It was clear and concise, not loud or boisterous, and he could hum the song to himself. The clocks called to each other and let their messages be heard. Even the smallest of clocks could sing and not be drowned out, and they continued to sing their song far past Zeris, into the mighty Altris. Every sound carried forth, and Haza Izmir was free now to listen to his clocks' music.

JULIA'S GREAT ADVENTURE

Little Julia knew well that every kid in town believed nuffi were magical beings, but she could never understand why. For being called fairies, they reminded her very much of herself, and *there isn't too much magical about that*, she thought. During the springtime, they often came out from their woods to adventure around the countryside and sell their goods. And it was during these times that word would spread from town to town and folks would curiously gather and eavesdrop, hoping to find out all they could about the mysterious nuffi. Yet these fairies were not foolish; they were always cautiously reserved and quiet and seldom spoke much about their crafts or hobbies. However, this garnered them even more attention, and all the kids, including Julia's many friends, were enthralled by the sight of them and talked about them as much as they could throughout the year.

What Julia came to gather through the many tales she heard was that these magical beings shared many enchanting properties with their fairy kin, but they looked quite different. They were larger than most other fairies, standing at about half the height of an adult human, and they had an almost humanlike appearance, and as such, the other six fairies—nymphs, cluricauns,[1] leprechauns, goblins, dryads, and gnomes—usually did not consider the nuffi fairies at all; they were never invited to fairy meetings or for fairy tea. "So what is so special about them?" Julia often said to her friends, and she received answers such as "Well, Windy Tim says that they put a spell on his cat and that it hasn't been the same since" or "Mrs. Pulter saw them stealing a whole lot of leeks from her field and then disappearing into thin air." It seemed almost probable, but Julia just wasn't sure about all of this talk. These tales sounded similar to the normal rumors that spread throughout the town of Hildur.

She wanted to ease her own curiosity. The only problem was that nuffi lived in the woods far away from humans and were seldom found around any major town, except during the springtime. No human and, more importantly, no kid had ever stepped inside the realm of the nuffi, and nuffi dwellings had become something of a folklore around the towns of the great realm of Trisden. Kids would think about great magic and wondrous spells, grand wizards, trees as tall as the tallest building they had ever seen, and many other great things, but none of this was fact; it was all myth and legend, for no one could confirm these beliefs, and many had tried. Kids and great adventurers alike had followed the trails into the woods in hopes of finding the famed realm, but every search met a similar ending of disappointment as all the would-be explorers turned back to town with little to report.

Yet this did not stop most kids from claiming that they had indeed found the major city of the nuffi. Some would brag and say that they had just heard the greatest spell or learned the most magical secret about the fairies, but most of the lot would find that each one was merely a fib and there was no truth to the matter at all. Julia had no intention of believing these false tales; they were too common, too similar, and far too time-consuming to hear. And most importantly, she was currently far too preoccupied with finding a gift for her mother and father's anniversary. The only story little Julia did happen to believe about the nuffi fairies was that they were great crafters; something she had seen with her own eyes when the fairies came to sell their wares in the local market.

These gifts, trinkets, and the like always glimmered and sparkled with a certain grandiosity. But Julia wondered what else nuffi could make with their magic and craftsmanship, considering her pa was a famous blacksmith worker and her mother was a master carpenter. Even more so, her brother, Alexander, the oldest of the bunch, was the apprentice blacksmith and her older sister, Lyria, was the apprentice carpenter, and they both had become quite good at producing their own splendid creations recently. So whatever gift Julia decided on had to be special; it had to be great.

When she woke up that day, she headed downstairs to the breakfast table and jovially greeted her brother and sister. "Good morning, Alex, good morning, Lyria," she said, before turning to her mother. "Good morning, Ma. Where's Pa?"

Her mother gave her a warm welcome and passed her a clean plate. "Early meeting in town with the rest of the blacksmith's guild today, Julia, but he should return soon. For the meantime, help yourself to some breakfast; we have eggs, toast, jam, and fruit."

"Jam is all finished," Alexander said.

"Why? You know it's my favorite," Julia grumbled.

"'Twasn't me, Lyria ate it all, Julia."

Lyria gave him a dirty look. "Alex, you always got to be lyin,' don't ya? Almost as bad as when you make up all of those false magical tales."

"There ain't no truth to that. All my tales are honest ones."

"You haven't gone more than an hour without a lie, Alex," Lyria said with a roll of her eyes as Julia lightly snickered.

Their mother interrupted them. "Everyone should enjoy their food and stop with the bickering. We all have a lot of work to do in the shop today."

Julia filled her plate and ate her breakfast, and when she was done, she readied herself to go into town. While her siblings and parents worked, she was tasked with getting some more cyrix root for the herbal tea her parents made. It was an easy task, and it was the perfect opportunity to find a gift for her parents. She only had a day left, and her options were not as plentiful as her hopes.

After buying the cyrix root that her mother preferred, Julia didn't have much money to spend, but she needed to show her appreciation somehow and some way. She went to the florist shop thinking she would find something grand to buy, but not many of the flowers were as pretty as she had hoped for, and the greatest of these were far too expensive for her pockets of paltry change. Next she went to the art gallery with the thought of getting a fine painting for the house, but nothing here was good enough for her either. At this point, Julia had no idea what to do or what to get, as she had gone to most of the stores and had few options left.

She continued her walk through town, though, and soon found a large cart where two nuffi merchants were selling a few of their wares to a local trader. Each item was expertly crafted, but she already knew she couldn't afford any of them, and most importantly, she knew most would not be all too different from items her ma or pa made. But a passing thought piqued a brilliant, wondering curiosity. "Maybe it'll be cheaper to get the goods directly from the source. And most importantly, there might be even more wonderful goods to be found in the nuffi realm that they don't bring to be sold here," she mumbled to herself.

Julia knew she had found the perfect solution and the perfect adventure. She cautiously looked around, and when no one was near, she slipped into the cart of the nuffi merchants. She hid among the nuffi wares and equipment and quietly covered herself with a small nuffi blanket. After a few minutes, the wagon began to move, and the traders were off, back to the realm of the nuffi without any knowledge of little Julia in the back of their cart. The journey was long, and Julia fell asleep for some time as they continued onward.

Several bumps and thuds along the way woke Julia from her nap. She took a moment to peek out the back of the wagon and gaze upon the tall trees of the unmarked forests. The roads were ones she had never seen before, and she had no idea where she was; she didn't even know if she was in the realm of Trisden anymore. "Sure is a pretty sight," she said to herself as she looked at the birds passing by and heard the sounds of the never-ending woods. The carriage cart soon came to a halt.

Julia made not a peep as one of the small fairies reached into the back of the wagon to grab some preserves to satisfy his hunger. As he moved through the equipment in the back and crept closer to Julia, she thought she would get caught. But the noises soon stopped as the little fairy found exactly what he was looking for and left the back of the luggage cart to head up front with his pal for the rest of the journey ahead.

Soon, after many hours of traveling, they finally made a long stop. Julia could hear the two nuffi talking and, from the conversation, knew that this was now the final stop on the journey. When she could no longer hear them, she slipped out the back of the wagon and checked that the area was clear before heading to find the cover of some dense flora atop a small hill.

Once she had secured a nice area for her to stay and rest, she looked out ahead and saw a great city among the dense trees. It was a wondrous and mysterious place that filled the forest with a brilliant luminance. Its roads continued deep past the furthest trees in her vision, and each pathway was filled with the activity of a plethora of nuffi, who were all fairly well-dressed. She knew now that she had found what everyone else had been searching for: it was the city of the nuffi from all the tales, and she was the first human to find it. Julia tried to contain her excitement as she stepped out to follow the path ahead carefully.

The city was different than any human town she had ever been in before; the buildings here were more similar to trees and large earthen huts than to normal houses, taverns, and stores. Crystal windows sparkled through wooden blinds and vine drapes, and varieties of colorful plants lit the roadways, guiding small carts and fairies throughout the city. There were plants and shrubs as big as houses, and some had actually been converted into such.

Julia wanted to explore it all, but she reminded herself that the most important goal was to get a gift for her parents, and she couldn't possibly do that without blending in with the rest of the crowd. Thankfully, Julia, at the age of nine, was about the same height as an adult nuffi. So she rummaged through a few carts parked on one of the lesser traveled roads on the outskirts of town until she found an old, worn nuffi hat, a pair of nuffi shoes, and a fine nuffi blazer, which all seemed to almost match one another. She then reminded herself well to return all of these items once she had found her gift.

But two concerns immediately came to Julia's mind: she might look like a nuffi, but she sure didn't know how to talk like one. And how would she even know the best gift to get or where to look? She

thought she could easily discover the answers by a little eavesdropping, which her ma and pa had always said wasn't respectful, but she felt this was at least a decent exception.

Now, most matters of nuffi conversations are different than those of human conversations, and for one who hasn't listened to a whole lot of nuffi talk, they might find themselves lost at first. But Julia was a fast learner, and she was sure she had enough patience to try and try until she knew as much as she could retain. The first group of nuffi she encountered in the city were cheery and pleasant, and their conversation was similar in style to their appearance.

"See, Faerafela, the sun surely shines splendidly on this side of town. Simply a spectacle for even the verdant heart flowers," the first nuffi said.

"I do agree, Rudil, but gloomy goes well with the glow of the gems gathered from the growing groves. The sun shan't have so much splendor all spring. 'Tis a nice mixture in both," the second quickly responded.

"Yes, Faerafela, maybe even better in summer. Till then, though, a fairly fairy spring will do. And for tea?"

"Yes, for two, indeed."

And with that they left, and poor Julia was ever confused, and I can't blame her a bit. The next conversation was a little tamer, though, and easier to understand, and most importantly, it seemed just the matter of common talk she was looking for.

"These are fine goods, Timli, but I surely say five fairy florals isn't fairly fair."

"That is the cheapest I can do, Dasi. A lot of work went into making these," the shopkeeper returned.

Now, Julia only had gild on her, which was common in most realms but not so common with fairies. And as you just heard, the fairies' preferred currency was florals, which was slightly cheaper than the standard piece of gild. But a going rate of five florals was still a decent price to pay, and little Julia checked her little pouch of gild to see exactly how much money she had saved from her chores over the last few months. "Four, five, six, seven," she said softly as her face lit up with certain excitement. "This is definitely enough to buy an item of worth for Ma and Pa."

Julia waited until the conversation was over and the fairy named Dasi had left the store, readying herself to make her own bargain with the shopkeeper. She remembered to try to speak and sound like a nuffi, and when she was fairly fairy certain she was ready, she went to the shopkeeper ready to buy.

"Hello, a fairly fairy good day to you," she said to Timli the shopkeeper with a smile—half of earnest respect, the other half of pride in her first attempt at being a nuffi.

"Hello, a fairly fairy good day to you as well, madam. What can I help you with today?" Timli said.

"I am looking for a special gift for a friend of mine, something unique and rare."

"Well, I make all these goods here myself, and I always put the finest bit of fairy craftsmanship and magic into every creation, so browse and let me know what piques your attention."

Julia went through the store, and she browsed till her heart was content. She picked up a few of the various items and put them back, and she mostly kept to herself. But the one thing she didn't truly know was nuffi customs. She would grab a beautifully studded statue, an antique jewelry chest, or a carefully casted teapot, take a brief look, and not say a word, which was often not the case with most nuffi, who were shy around humans but talkative among their own kind.

"I haven't seen you around here before," Timli said. "Do you live in Faeril?" This was, of course, the name of the city, and Julia just learned this, just like you and I did.

She thought for a moment of what to say. "Yes, but I live on the other side of town, and I don't usually come to market often. I try to save my money," she said with a smile, but she was panicking quite a bit. Julia felt her cover fleeing, so she quickly eyeballed a nice crystal ornament and brought it to the front of the store. "How much for this piece here?"

"That will be six fairy florals," Timli said.

Julia grabbed her coin pouch and produced her seven pieces of gild. "I plan to pay in gild, if that is alright."

Timli looked at the gild with a brewing curiosity. He scratched his fairy beard and gave Julia a curious gaze. "I don't see gild around here too often. Well, not from nuffi who usually don't come to market, that is. Where in Faeril did you say you lived?"

Julia panicked even more now, as she had not a clue of what to say. Timli fiddled around with the florals he had in his register, producing a quarter floral to return for what would be about a five-gild payment, but he was waiting for a response to his question. Julia had not yet provided an answer.

He sat there and produced a nervous look, as if he had seen something grave. "I think I know well what this all is, now," he anxiously said, raising his voice, but not in a rude way. "You are a human!" he proclaimed. "It must be true."

A few nuffi who were outside the shop stopped their various tasks and looked towards Timli and Julia. "A human," one of them shrieked, which only caused a few more nuffi to stop going about their usual tasks, and the process continued in the same motion until nearly the whole city of Faeril knew about the human impostor.

Julia was frozen with fear; she had no idea what would happen now that the nuffi had discovered the truth. "We must bring her to the mayor at once; he'll know what to do from here," one of the nuffi said, which brought a lot of agreeable murmuring among the gathering crowd. "Yes, we must do this at once," another said. And with that, Julia was led along through Faeril, followed by droves of nuffi, until she approached the grand manor of the mayor of Faeril. The silver gate opened the way to a beautiful cobblestone pathway that led to the front steps of the manor. Ivy vines trickled down the stalwart pillars, and ivy leaves adorned the elegant walnut doors, which opened in all the commotion to reveal an older nuffi with wild gray hair.

"What seems to be the meaning of this wondrous wayfaring about Faeril?" the mayor asked.

Timli now stepped forward from among the crowd and cordially greeted the mayor. "Well, Elberi, it seems that a human child happened to find her way into the center of Faeril, and we first discovered her within my shop."

The mayor's face creased with a great confusion. "Humans never make it this deep into the woods of Trisden. And if they do, we always have a way for shooing them away before they get too close to discovering our peaceful city. If one has made it here, now they will all come, and Faeril will become just as noisy and confused as any other human town," he said with a great shake of his shaggy head.

"She was very clever and dressed and acted like one of us," Timli said.

Elberi now motioned towards Timli. "Bring her forward, so that I may speak with her in person." With that, there was a bunch of commotion in the crowd, and soon there was a small parting, and from it finally emerged Julia, still wearing the nuffi hat, blazer, and shoes. She looked upon the mayor, who stood about the same height as her, and she couldn't help but feel nervous.

But Elberi just sighed with tired calmness. "What is your name? And what brings you to Faeril?"

Julia took off the nuffi hat and gripped it tightly with both her hands. "Julia," she lightly spoke. "And I came here because I wanted to get my parents a special gift, and the talk around Trisden is that nuffi make some of the finest crafts."

Elberi agreeably nodded. "Who says this?"

"All of the townsfolk in Hildur that I know. And all my friends tell tales about fairies, and everyone says that nuffi are very magical but aren't like other fairies. I was always curious as to why, but no one I know has ever visited a fairy town, so I wanted to find out the answer for myself."

"Your curiosity stirred a great commotion in town and put a lot of fairies through a great deal of anxious sorts. But your intentions were earnest, and you seem a simple soul. The best thing to do is to send you back on your way, but with your ingenuity, I have another idea for now. There is a great fairy council to take place tomorrow, the Fantastical Fairy Association of Trisden. All of the great fairies in Trisden take part: goblins, gnomes, cluricauns, leprechauns, dryads, and nymphs—all except the nuffi. We have tried for centuries to get into the council, but we never were invited, not even to speak.

However, as a human you talk differently than the fairies of Trisden; they'll surely think you are an outsider fairy, and an impartial voice to speak on behalf of the nuffi might be just what we need."

Julia was surely excited about the prospect of meeting other fairies, and the Fantastical Fairy Association of Trisden—the F.F.A.T., for short—sounded marvelous, but she couldn't help but feel that this would leave her barely any time to return to town and find a gift. And all she currently had to bring home was the cyrix root, and that wouldn't do on its own. "When is the meeting?" Julia said.

"Noontime, of course; every matter is always discussed over noon tea! Now, I shall send a letter to the F.F.A.T. by way of owl messenger to ask for the acceptance of you as a one-day ambassador for the nuffi. They should surely accept."

"Is it a business sort of meeting? Because I don't know much about professional matters, especially that of fairies," Julia humbly said.

Elberi nodded his head. "It will be a fancy fairy affair, so we must prepare. You must dress for the occasion, and those clothes will surely not do. The rest of what to say and do is all up to you. If you are smart enough to find our city, you will speak just fine, and an earnest speech is the best form of talk."

The owl messenger was soon sent, and in a little more than an hour it returned with a reply. The fairies anxiously waited in silence and refrained from their impromptu tea party, which had started the moment the letter had been sent off. Elberi quickly opened the letter and turned to the crowd of nuffi with a grand smile. "Julia will speak on behalf of the nuffi at the meeting tomorrow." The nuffi cheered, and for the rest of the day, all Julia heard was various notes of encouragement and pieces of advice from the fairies. "Be careful what you say around those goblins and cluricauns; they are a nasty and mischievous bunch," and "Make sure you compliment the dryads on their sylvan magic," and lastly, "Don't stare at the nymphs or they might be offended."

All Julia thought was that this was a completely different feeling from when they first discovered that she was human. The nuffi trusted her, and had even grown quite fond of her presence. They whispered among themselves that maybe humans weren't so troublesome to have as friends. In the evening, the nuffi made sure she had the best accommodations: she had fine fruits, vegetables, and assorted breads and grains with fancy fairy juice for dinner, and they even made her a dessert of finely assorted ices and creams. When she was finished, Julia was given the finest fairy bed, and it was just the perfect size. She went to bed early to make sure to prepare for her meeting, and she dreamed of the wonders of the other fairies, which she would soon see in reality.

The following morning, she was greeted with a breakfast that was just as luxurious as the dinner the night before. And when it was near time for the meeting, the mayor personally arranged for a carriage to pick up Julia. For about an hour the carriage traveled deeper and deeper into the woods of Trisden. The trees radiated with magical colors, and various flowers and mushrooms grew all around the rocky dirt road. There were verdant heart flowers, ruby-stone shrooms, and many other plants and fungi she couldn't identify. When the carriage stopped, the small nuffi chauffeur came to open the cart door and lent Julia a hand out of the carriage. He looked up at the sky and thought for a moment.

"Miss Julia," the nuffi chauffeur, whose name was Fanfir, said, "we seem to be just in time for the start of the meeting. Follow me, and I will bring you within a few hundred meters of the gathering, and the rest of the magic shall be up to you."

After a hundred paces or so in the deep woods, Julia could hear some faint talking, and it grew louder with every step. Through a small clearing of beautiful berry bright bale bushes Fanfir abruptly stopped in his tracks and turned to Julia with the tip of his small nuffi top hat. "Miss Julia, here I must leave you. I will wait back at the carriage for you for when the meeting is done. You shall give a most splendid presentation for all the nuffi today; I know it well as the woods be wonderful."

Julia gave a delightful smile. "Thank you, Fanfir. I shall see you soon then." And with that, they both parted for now, and Julia headed off to the meeting. Once she lost sight of Fanfir, the forest began to open up before her, and the radiant glow of the flora was now complemented by piercing rays of brilliant light, and soon she was in a clearing where a large round circle of fine wooden and ivy chairs was situated around a small central mound. Around these chairs was the most brilliant sight: it was the rest of the fairy groups of Trisden; they were all present, just like the nuffi had told her they would be.

There among them were the tricky cluricauns, the crafty gnomes, the strong dryads, the impish goblins, the shy nymphs, and the jolly leprechauns. There were more fairies than Julia could count. Some wore fancy clothes and others wore little at all; some were pale green, and others had fur covering parts of their body. And they each had a leader to represent them at the meeting. Julia could barely contain her excitement; she had so many questions, but she knew she had to be professional and give a good impression on behalf of the nuffi.

Now, among the fairies, a rather old gnome with a large gray beard went to the central mound and grabbed a tiny wooden mallet. He patiently, but with steady conviction, gave three solid smacks of the gavel on the small wooden podium in front of him. "Attention, fairies of Trisden. A fantastical fairy day to you all, and a great welcome to the 431st Annual Gathering of the Fantastical Fairy Association of Trisden. There are many items to discuss today, so we must begin on schedule. Grab your fairy tea, crumpets, and jam, and take your seats so that we may proceed."

Julia tried her best to blend in with the crowd as they hurried over to their seats. There was no assigned seating, so it was a confused frenzy of sorts. But she made sure to heed the advice from yesterday and avoided sitting too close to the cluricauns or the goblins while trying to find a seat near the leprechauns or the gnomes, who were often more well-mannered. Most of the fairies talked among themselves about a multitude of different fairy matters before a great silence arose and all attention focused on the central podium.

The old gnome shuffled around a few papers in his hand and looked around at the rest of the fairies. "I believe my sight and senses were a lot better at one hundred and forty-nine," he heartily said with a chuckle. A good deal of laughing was had among the rest of the fairies. "But I do see a lot of familiar faces: Fulgul Ferwickle of the goblins of East Bogswurd; Elda Magalilli of the gnomes of Stelford;

Alryn Delpi of the dryads of Delphus; Persena Relda of the nymphs of Fairdew Forest; Halwill Coryl of the leprechauns of Little Mellow Meadow; and Delwell Justi of the cluricauns of Misty Flower Woods. It is a pleasure to see you all again. Now, without further delay, let us go over the talking points for the meeting."

The little gnome quickly glanced down at his papers. "The faith and value placed in the fairy floral has been raised as a point of concern."

A burst of commotion came from the side of the cluricauns. "Maybe if the gnomes stopped switching over to gild, there wouldn't be that problem," Delwell the cluricaun said, as he gave a wicked glance at Elda and her group.

"Maybe if the cluricauns stopped looting, there would be more faith placed in fairies to conduct proper business," Elda returned. The two groups began to bicker between one another; it was no secret that the gnomes and the cluricauns rarely got along, and they didn't hold back here. One of the cluricauns even took off one of his fairy shoes and threw it, but it was a tiny shoe, and it missed its mark by quite a bit.

"Please, please, there must be order," Persax pleaded. "Let us move on to the next point and save currency for later. The dispute with the ogres of Windy Walnut Way," the old gnome said, which was soon met with more chatter.

"Don't blame the goblins," Fulgul said. "It is more the fault of the dryads than anyone else." The goblins and the dryads now argued and another shoe was thrown—this time by one of the goblins, who don't normally wear shoes, so they grabbed one of the leprechaun's shoes. Fairies hardly have good aim, so this also missed.

"Okay, okay, maybe a point we all can agree on," Persax said, taking a little handkerchief out from his pocket to wipe the sweat from his forehead.

"Well, the fairy tea is awful, how about that?" Alryn said, making a rather unpleasant face.

"I second that," Fulgul said. "It tastes like rather unpleasant bog water."

"Well, all bog water I would think is unpleasant, but I third this," Elda said.

"And I fairy fourth it," Delwell said.

Persax shook his head and rubbed his forehead and his eyes. "I made that tea with a lot of care."

"And a lot of bad tea leaves," Halwill said, and all the other fairies laughed.

"Let us move past the tea for now," Persax said with another pat of the handkerchief along his forehead. "The nuffi have sent an ambassador to speak on their behalf, a fairy from out of Trisden, hailing from the leprechauns in Eurus, I believe, yes?" Persax said, as he looked towards Julia.

Julia froze for a second and wished she had asked Elberi what type of fairy she was to be before departing from Faeril. "Yes," she said timidly.

"Splendid, well, come here to the center of the group and introduce yourself. Let us hear what you have to say on behalf of the nuffi."

Julia slowly rose from her seat and looked around; all of the fairies were looking directly at her. When she approached the center podium, Persax shook her hand. "What is your name?" he said.

Julia hadn't even thought of a fairy name, and this made her particularly nervous. "Julia," she said.

"A rather odd name for a fairy, but who am I to say. Please, do tell us more." The whole forest was silent. Julia had no idea what to say; she didn't know the first thing about pretending to be a leprechaun.

"A fairly fairy day to you all," she opened with. "My name is Julia, and I am from Ironbeak Hills in Eurus." All of the fairies looked at each other. Ironbeak Hills was a real place, but it was located in Middrit, not Eurus. "I have been fairly fairy friends with the nuffi for many years, and I visit them all the time when I travel to Trisden."

The leprechauns looked at each other with suspicion. "How about a basic bit of fairy magic?" Halwill said.

Julia froze, and her eyes grew wide. "I don't think I am prepared right now."

"We leprechauns don't practice as much magic as other fairies, so just a little presentation should be fine," Halwill said, as he and the rest of the fairies patiently waited.

Julia tried to think of something clever, but a moment later the crowd appeared to be lost. "She is no fairy, not even a leprechaun! This is just a nuffi trick!" Alryn said. Everyone began to bicker and argue. And, following what now appeared to be custom, another shoe was thrown.

Once Persax had calmed the group down again, he turned to Julia. "Who exactly are you, and what are you doing here at our meeting?"

Julia let out a small nervous sigh. "My name is Julia, and I am a just a small girl who found her way into the capital of the nuffi by stowing away in one of their travel carts. But even though I am not a fairy, I still think the nuffi should be invited to your annual meetings like the rest of the fairies here."

"A nonfairy can't speak about fairy matters," Fulgul prominently proclaimed. "The human girl probably doesn't even have an ounce of magic about her whole being."

This was a very rude thing to say, and was quite untrue, as magic takes all forms in all things. Julia put her head down with disappointment, but a clever idea began to blossom in her mind, and a courage stirred within her heart. She still had the cyrix root her mother had sent her out to get for tea. "Let me see a cup of tea," she said aloud. "I will perform a bit of my own magic."

Fulgul gave Julia his cup. "Only a divine being can fix Persax's terrible tea." The rest of the fairies laughed. Julia took the small fairy cup, which was much smaller than the average human cup, and reached into the bag of cyrix root. She put a little of the herb into the cup of tea and then handed it back to Fulgul. "Take a sip and tell me that it isn't better," Julia proudly said.

Fulgul was quite hesitant. After smelling the tea for a few seconds, he took a small sip. At first, he tried to hide his satisfaction by making a grumpy face—which isn't all too hard for a goblin to do, especially one as grumpy as Fulgul—but he couldn't deny that the tea was simply splendid. "This is quite good, better than we ever had at Fairy Association meetings," he relented.

The rest of the fairies' eyes glimmered with excitement; fairies, of course, do love their tea. "What sorcery is contained within that bag?" Persena said. The other fairies were all raving—they wanted to try a taste of this special tea. Julia happily produced the bag and helped flavor all of the fairies' teas with the cyrix root until there was only a little herb left.

The fairies, all now happily enjoying their tea, were quiet and content, and Persax was beyond ecstatic. "This is the best-behaved I have ever seen the other fairies. What is that herb called, and where did you find such a delicacy?"

"I can tell you all about it, but first I must humbly insist that the nuffi are made members of the Fairy Association," Julia said.

Persax smiled. "The nuffi owe you more than you can imagine. Anyone who can produce such good fairy tea and bring order to an F.F.A.T. meeting shall have their request. And if it is to allow the nuffi into the association, well, consider it granted, Julia!" There were great elations and cheers among the fairies, and when the meeting was over, it was time for Julia to head back to meet Fanfir at the carriage. She told him the splendid news, and he was simply overjoyed.

"I knew you could do it, Julia! Elberi and the rest of the nuffi will be ecstatic! Now let us get back to Faeril. Good news like this deserves a timely introduction!"

When they entered Faeril, the nuffi had gathered around the city square in anticipation of the news Julia was bringing. Elberi greeted her, and Julia gave a happy nod. "The nuffi are allowed in the Fantastical Fairy Association of Trisden." The nuffi cheered and a huge party was thrown. There was berry bright bale pie, ruby-stone shroom quiche, and of course, fairy tea. Julia was so happy, and what made her even happier was that Elberi and the nuffi presented her with a gem-studded gold ring for her mother and a matching gem-studded gold watch for her father for their anniversary. Even more so, Persax, on behalf of the F.F.A.T., had sent a wonderfully ornate tea set to Faeril for Julia. Now Julia certainly had a wonderful adventure to tell when she arrived back in town.

After the celebrations, Fanfir and the grand nuffi carriage traveled back to the town of Hildur and dropped Julia in front of her house just in time for the family celebration, and with a wondrous wave, Fanfir was off, back to Faeril. Julia presented the gifts to her parents, which they loved, and the anniversary celebrations were fantastically grand. And from this moment on, not only were the nuffi included in the F.F.A.T., but at every fairy party, fairy wedding, and fairy gathering—to which Julia always had a cordial invitation—as well as just in plain everyday use, cyrix root was added to fairy tea, which was surely splendid. And they had Julia and her great adventure to thank for that.

The Marker of Tides

CHAPTER 1

A Place by the Sea

It was a cool, crisp September morning that brought George Wendersen out to watch the ocean from his front porch for the first time in many months. The sight was as pleasant as he could remember: the air was fresh, the water clear, and the beach ahead of him was his own to enjoy. He kept to his usual daily routine of drinking tea—taking a rather large chug—and pacing up and down the cedar boards of his deck, until a tiredness overcame his legs and he finally took to one of the two rocking chairs that faced eastward towards the sea.

The waves crashed and clamored, subsequently resolving to a permeating cadence of solitude as the foamy water crept up upon the sandy shoals and jagged rocks of the beach. George ran his hand through his short light-gray hair and took a deep breath as he reclined in his chair and gently rocked back and forth. He kept his eyes focused ahead, letting only his ears occasionally deviate from the sound of the ocean as the invariable *squeak* from his chair pierced the air and lent itself to memory. He momentarily looked at the rocking chair adjacent to him but quickly returned his focus to the beach. Yet, his resiliency failed him; his vision was no longer concentrated. The corner of his eyes had become more conscious, and his vision jaded. He anxiously tapped his hand against the arm of his chair; something had to go, something had to change.

He continued to watch the waves, quickly finishing his tea while occupying his mind with the thought of getting another cup. But he wasn't thirsty, not even close, so he left the porch and, with a certain sense of conviction, prepared for his walk into town to begin the busy day ahead.

The road was long, but he walked it in an unbridled state of celerity, an unmistakable mark of his predilection for efficiency, a most alert form of consciousness that had produced an old, tired, successful man. For you see, George was an efficacious businessman with an ardent charisma for achievement that mostly juxtaposed the ethos of the simple seafaring town of Carlington. Most of the population had come to know only a few ways of life: fishing, blacksmithing, woodworking, cooking, or shipbuilding. Mr. Wendersen, as most of the townsfolk called him, did not dabble in any of the aforementioned pursuits; rather, he owned most of the land that had produced such opportunities.

Almost every other street of Carlington contained at least one property George had sold or owned, and it did him good to see what business thrived on his land. To him, everything was business, but it was good business and, above all, fair business. He had built the foundations that housed many dreams, and though he sold more properties than he kept, he believed that most of the townsfolk of Carlington owed their success to his hard work.

He was a savvy opportunist but maintained morality in all of his dealings; for such, he earned not the ire of any man or woman in the town of Carlington or any other town along the spanning coastline of the land of Eurus. The local folk waved to George as he walked through town. "Fine day, Mr. Wendersen," "A good morning to you, Mr. Wendersen," and "Wonderful to see you, Mr. Wendersen," they said with amiable greetings on this rather sunny morning. He returned with a smile and a genial nod, and occasionally with a greeting of his own.

He started a conversation with a few of his tenants and neighbors of each property, making sure to keep himself well-informed about local matters while he walked through every inch of town looking for future endeavors to embark on. It was good for him to always keep moving; stagnation was never a viable option, and as such, he seldom relaxed, indulging every so often in leisure only if he believed doing so would produce more energy for work. However, lately the end of his trips had focused on a personal task that he felt was most necessary for him to complete.

So, with most of the day still ahead of him and his errands finished, he entered his favorite general store, Tom's Merchandises, to pick up materials that he desperately needed for his personal work. The sun shined through the many storefront windows, gracing the aged cedar interior of the quaint store that had been a staple of Carlington for many generations. George remembered many years ago when Tom Sr. had sat behind the counter every day greeting customers—a job that had now been passed on to his son, Tom Jr., who ran the store all by himself. George grabbed his favorite set of stationery paper and envelopes, then quickly added the local newspaper before putting all of the items on top of the counter and waiting for the clerk.

An old man came from the back of the store and cracked a smile as he saw George standing in front of the counter. "Hey, George, I was not expecting to see you here today! How have you been feeling? Any better?"

"I'm doing fine, Tom," George quickly returned. "I saw you just last week. Things couldn't have changed much since then."

"Things change every day, most of the time whether we like them to or not. Either way, I'm glad to see you. Maybe you can give me a good conversation to help pass the day! Most folk only come in here to get their goods and be on their way. They are like the wind, especially the ones I've known for many years."

"Then I think you might be scaring them away, Tom."

Tom lightly laughed. "Could very well be so. And might just as well be indicative of the company I still keep—good principles, bad habits!"

George cracked a smile while he politely took his items from Tom and paid the total. He had nothing else to say and was determined to go about town and read his newspaper before quickly heading home, but Tom was intent on talking for a little longer. He was just that type of person: a kind soul who didn't refrain from saying what was on his mind, always thinking that his words might help whomever he was talking with.

"If you ask me, I think you should take it easy, George. Maybe, get away from all this writing that you've been doing. All these letters can't be good for you. It does no good for the mind to keep obsessing about something in the past."

"Tom, we have had this conversation before, and I would rather not have it again." George could have easily walked out of the shop, but he couldn't help but feel that he needed to hear what else Tom had to say.

"All I mean to say is that sometimes it's best to drop whatever is bothering you and give yourself something to do, even if you have nothing planned: make something up. There are a lot of better things to occupy your time with than working all day and then going home to write letters to someone who is not even reading them."

George grimaced; he was annoyed for not having left sooner. He had nothing but respect for Tom and he didn't have an ounce of malice in his heart for anyone or anything, but he did not want to hear any more guidance about how to navigate through his supposed problem. He kept his response short and precise, as was customary for most of his dealings. "Maybe one day I will take your advice, but for now I am too set on making the most out of these envelopes and paper that I just purchased."

Tom laughed. "Well, I'll be here when you need to get some more. Till then, take good care of yourself, old friend."

George waved goodbye to Tom and walked through town. The streets were alive with the sound of commerce, but George had had enough of business for one day. It was no news that Carlington was a modern, prosperous town, but to those that truly knew it best, it was, above all, a seaside town. George passed by an empty lot he owned as he walked to the boardwalk to find a quiet, shady spot to read his newspaper. Once he found the perfect spot, he read a few articles, skimmed through the pages, and discovered a short piece about the establishment of a small chapel within Carlington.

He looked back towards his vacant lot in the distance. He couldn't explain it at first, but the prospect of the new chapel piqued his interest. It wasn't his ordinary business venture, but it was a nice change from his normal way of thinking.

When he finished his paper, he left the comfort of the shade to continue his walk and passed by a small restaurant. He had sold the land two years prior and now stopped to witness what wonder that small lot had turned into. He looked in the windows and saw a multitude of families and couples sitting and eating, and he stood and stared a little longer till his legs began to tire, at which point he decided to leave the town of Carlington to its sunset and continue on home. It was a four-mile journey that seemed a lot longer now on the return than it had earlier in the morning. But George cared little for this; he was a fit and strong man for the age of seventy-six, and the exercise was happily welcomed.

He entered his house and quickly made himself another cup of tea as he looked around the dimly lit rooms. Every space had its own collection of fine wares and antique furniture; most luxurious rugs draped the floors in warm embraces, and beautiful curtains veiled the sight offered by each window. Soon, the luminous glow from a small desk lamp cut through the darkness: George grabbed his tea, took out his stationery, and began to think of a few ideas on what to write. He selected his favorite fountain pen, dipped it in his favorite jar of sapphire-colored ink, and jotted down a few notes, hoping to make this letter far better than the last. After about an hour or so of writing sentences that he deemed unfit and wasting almost half a dozen sheets of stationery, George let out a deep sigh and stared blankly at a fresh sheet of paper.

The words were in the forefront of his mind: he could feel it, he just needed to write them. If only he could somehow not overthink it, he knew he could turn his ideas into a beautiful letter. His pen was more than worthy of the job, and he trusted that it would lend itself well if he believed himself apt to write. It took some convincing, but the words began to slowly flow and continued to increase in quantity until the letter was soon complete; it was concise, but it was more meaningful than George felt he had ever been in his entire life. Finished, he read it aloud:

Dearest Gertrude,

I looked at the waves today, just like we used to do. It was a beautiful sight, something that I had not allowed myself to enjoy in quite some time. I sat there for as long as my heart would allow, but I quickly became lost—the feeling just wasn't the same. I took a walk through town to tend to my work and occupy my mind, and I bought some stationery so that I may write this letter. It seems that little has changed in Carlington, but everything surely feels different to me.

I wanted to write about you, Gertrude, but there are no words I can think of that would be fitting for your grace. I cannot understand your feelings, your intricacies, or the pain that you feel. For whatever I did, I am truly sorry, and whatever it takes to fix such wrongs, I will gladly do; but please, I am old and set to view matters in one way, and, hitherto, I dared not dabble in how to do it any other. If only I may know what trouble I have caused, I will fix it; I promise you this. I hope that this letter may at least allow me to hear from you again, and maybe one day when you come back home, we can look at the waves together again and reminisce about the many good memories we shared.

Love,
George

He was nearly exhausted now and could not dare muster the strength to walk upstairs to bed; the couch would have to do for the night. He readied his letter to be mailed tomorrow. He hoped to hear from his wife and maybe gain a semblance of wholeness back into his life. He tried to ease himself to sleep, but his mind whirled and thoughts cluttered his head. He dared not dream on this night but hoped to just close his eyes and go off to sleep to wake the next morning with many new things to occupy his mind.

CHAPTER 2

ROADS OF TOMORROW

Many days had passed, and George counted every single one of them since he had mailed his letter. It was now twenty-two days. He made a point not to forget it—twenty-two whole days. *Maybe the carrier cart was slow*, he thought to himself. *Or she can't figure out what to say. Or maybe the letter arrived today and is waiting at home.* He ran through the list of options until it gave him a headache and until the time arrived to attend to other plans.

There was a great idea brewing in his mind—a brilliant one, in fact—and he couldn't pass on the opportunity. It was something that might prove to be a worthy respite from the thought of Gertrude. He was so excited, and he made sure everything was ready for his meeting ahead. He walked to town and arrived at his vacant plot of land, which was situated only four blocks from the coastline.

He had been showing the land to many interested buyers over the past few months, but this meeting provided a unique promise, and he was in need of a change: maybe it might just do some good for him. George was planning to meet with the mayor and run through the features of the property and all that it could offer the town if they chose to build here. If all came to fruition, it would be one of the most splendid chapels and community centers within fifty miles of Carlington.

George was early, just as planned. He looked over every inch of his land. "I could get much more for this property," he said with a modicum of newfound doubt as he thought over the list of potential buyers who would be interested in the land. "But it is a fair deal, and a good deal. There will be much wealth to be found here when all is said and done!" He ended his mental soliloquy with optimism as the mayor approached from afar.

"Good morning to you, George," the mayor happily said.

"Good morning, Catherine. Good to see you," he returned.

"I cannot begin to thank you enough for entertaining the request of the town and allowing me to take a look at your land today."

"I am happy to show my land to anyone who is interested. There is no reason at all to thank me. Besides, I am quite delighted to hear of the work that you are doing. There is much merit to be found in the construction of a chapel in Carlington."

"Yes, we will hope to see many people in the community use this building for a variety of different events. It will be a place dedicated to the community, a place that will help every citizen in Carlington!"

George smiled at the thought. He hadn't found much to smile about lately. "It sounds magnificent, Catherine." He motioned ahead. "Let us then get started." He led Catherine through the property and discussed with her every feature of the land. Everything was perfect: the plot was large, the land had no issues, and the price was fair.

The mayor was impressed and she did not try to hide it when she talked to George. "This seems like the perfect location for the chapel. There are a few matters that I will have to discuss further with the committee, but everything is just as expected. If it is quite alright, I will write you by next week!"

George was happy with her answer. He gave his farewells to Catherine and proceeded into town, intent on making the most of his day. Passing by the buildings nearest to the sea, he decided to take a bit of advice from his friend Tom and stroll down the boardwalk. As per usual, most of the folk greeted him, and he gave pleasant greetings in return. It felt particularly good to walk leisurely about and return to a sense of comfort. The ocean water was as beautiful as ever. He felt good today, far better than in days past. He hoped now, more than ever, to make that trend continue.

CHAPTER 3

THE LAST LETTER

During the subsequent days, George completed many relaxing activities throughout town. He went for a walk along the shore, visited a few of his tenants' restaurants for leisure rather than business, and allotted enough time to enjoy the last few days of the beautiful summer weather. When he arrived home after each day, he was too tired to focus on anything but the next day ahead. His stationery sat on his desk at home, and he had no urge to write letters; he was quite content with his time.

He prepared a few business documents for the next meeting with the mayor and asked his lawyer to prepare the workings of an agreement and procure the deed to the property. His lawyer, a meticulous and shrewd man, frowned at the thought of such a deal. "George, you can do much better," he ardently proclaimed. "Think of all the profit you are losing by selling this property to the town. There are numerous business owners who would pay nigh twice the amount the town is offering you for this land. It is an untenable proposition!"

George knew well that his lawyer was right in his summary of the fiscal error of the current situation, but, for once, he didn't care so much about that. There was more to value in this deal than just tangible assets; there was something important that he couldn't quite describe with the typical business language he was so used to using with his associates.

"I will think it all over, and I shall write you a letter with what I plan to do. I bought some new stationery that I am not using for anything else," he said with a smile as he ended the meeting short and gave a quick farewell. He felt good, like a wave of relief had swept away his burdens, and on his walk through town he passed by Tom's Merchandises and decided to stop in and say hello.

"Here to give me business again? That was quite a quick time to go through a set of stationery," Tom jovially said as George walked into the shop.

"No, not today, my friend. I am here only to talk."

Tom's face displayed an obvious look of shock. "To talk! This is a great honor that you have bestowed upon me! What shall we toast to?" he happily said, as he poured a cup of tea for George and himself.

"To days well spent—and with good company, of course," George jovially said and shared a laugh with Tom. They continued to recall and share many great memories and good times, and George had surely found a great semblance of happiness in what seemed like a very dark time in his life. For the first time in many months, he felt lifted from the burden of his sadness, and he intended to not look back but only look forward to new days ahead.

He walked home rather late, later than he was accustomed to, and was surprised to find a letter waiting for him in his mailbox. The prior events of the day seemed to fade to a place where he could no longer reach them, and he reluctantly grasped onto all that was left before him. He felt the letter in his hand and turned it over slowly, looking at the writing with a fluttered breath; it was Gertrude's. He anxiously opened his house door and sat down on the couch in his living room. He carefully opened the letter and read it aloud:

Dear George,

I have a stack of your letters near me, and I was intent on leaving this one alone just like the others, but I felt inclined to answer your question. I don't think you are aware just how self-centered you have been over the span of your life. Everything was always business to you, George, and I hope you shall learn to move away from such a lifestyle. There is no point of procuring such wealth if you are not capable of giving it away when it matters most. Alas, I believe it is too late for you to truly change your ways and renounce your past. For the future, all I can hope is that you are able to find some peace in everything that you do. There is no chance for us to work this all out. There is too much pain to mend and too little time to reconcile all the issues. I am just as tired as you are, and I need a break from all of this; I need some time to enjoy the rest of my life. I wish you well, George, and I hope you take care of yourself.

Sincerely,
Gertrude

George put the letter down and stared blankly at the living room wall: he was in shock. A sickness took hold of him, and his stomach felt near empty. His throat swelled, and his heart pained him. He ran his hand through his hair and put his head down. He had nothing left to do, nothing else to think of. All of his attempts to put Gertrude behind him was for naught: he was nothing without her. There was no purpose in him moving on. All he could think about was what he had lost when she had walked out of his life. He had foolishly dabbled in the thought of enjoying a peaceful life, but he was all alone, and it was too late to make new friends in the community of Carlington. He slowly stood up, expending nearly the last bit of energy he could muster in the process. He wanted to just go to sleep and forget this all happened, but it was not that simple. He felt that there had to be something he could do to win her back; there had to be something he could do to rid himself of this pain.

A thought of Gertrude smiling entered his head. He remembered just how happy she had been when he had bought her parents a boat, so that they could enjoy the ocean. The boat wasn't much, but he had saved ever piece of gild he made to buy it. It seemed like a lifetime ago, but it was still his life, and now he had the means to do even more. He had more wealth now than ever before, but he needed something grand to win her back. He grinned suddenly. A different tone took over his voice. "I have the means to gather more wealth than imaginable. I can save up just like I did those many years ago, and when she sees what I have procured in my devotion, I can give it away! Every bit earned spent in charity for her return. It will be the same generosity that made her happy to love me those many years ago. That is just what I'll do, and I won't delay."

The days came and went, and George stuck to his usual routine of speaking to his tenants and roaming around town. His business dealings became personal, and his personal matters became business. Though his intent seemed earnest, what was once fairness now became greed, and he began to raise the rent on his tenants. He saw wealth as the only opportunity to see the return of his wife. And the proud reputation he had maintained soon became sullied, and he earned the ire of every person in Carlington.

He thought of the chapel. It was a fine deal, but to George, to the new man he had become, there were better uses for such property, and he could not afford to lose money on such a notable pursuit. The agreements, the deed—all of it he refused to produce; he reneged on the deal. Catherine was shocked. The fine man that she knew had destroyed the hopes of the townsfolk and taken away any chance that the chapel would have a fine location in Carlington.

George sold his land for nigh twice the amount and procured a great deal more wealth, but it was not yet enough for him. When he walked down the streets of town, the men and women of Carlington turned their backs on him. They knew just what he had done and how selfish he had become. They did not want to call him Mr. Wendersen anymore; they did not even want to look at him. All he was to them was a wretched, poor old man.

But George could not have cared less if no one greeted him on his walks. He believed they would change their minds, just as Gertrude would change her mind, when he gave all of the wealth away, all back to the town. They would love him more than they ever had. So he kept to his business, refraining to deviate from his set path.

After one successful day, he decided to return home to enjoy the comforts of his house. Alas, he entered only to see it in shambles: the door busted wide open; the fine jewelry, antiques, and furniture all stolen; the safe he had kept filled with money taken away. *I have more though*, he thought. *I own my properties, many properties!* This brought him needed comfort in this dark time.

Unfortunately, George had unfairly raised the rents on his properties and word had quickly spread of his avarice. Over the upcoming months, his tenants began to leave, seeking other places for their businesses. New tenants stayed away; they couldn't afford the rent and didn't want to deal with a man like George. The people in town hated every aspect of him and his properties were soon vandalized.

George was devastated. He didn't know what to do, and he had little wealth left, if any at all. He spent whatever money he had invested in banks to restore his buildings, but his efforts could not restore his reputation. He tried to rest in his house, but there was nothing to go back to. He was all alone; all of his wealth had been taken as a result of his own selfish pursuits, and so he stayed at home waiting for something, or maybe for someone, to help him.

CHAPTER 4

UPON OCEAN'S TIDES

The next morning, he awoke and carried himself down the stairs into his living room, where before his eyes stood his wife, Gertrude. She must have heard of his troubles, for within the cold, dimly lit house, his love had returned. George was ecstatic, happy now, even after losing everything. Whatever troubles he had endured, he could now surely fix them. With Gertrude by his side, he had everything he could have ever wanted; and the town of Carlington presented itself in a new light, and the man that everyone had come to know as Mr. Wendersen was content: something he had never been in his entire life.

Of all the things he had wished for, nothing was greater than to sit by the sea with his wife and follow the waves from their initial conception to the ultimate culmination of their beauty upon the shore. And so George and Gertrude went out to the porch and sat in their rocking chairs looking at the sea. He could think of the past without regret, approach the future with a certain calm conviction, and focus on the present with patience. The ocean was a beautiful sight: it was the culmination of his life in one view, and it was George's to share with his wife forever. He smiled as he looked at Gertrude and then stared out into the endless ocean. A cool wind blew, rattling the one chair, moving it furiously back and forth, and George's chair stood still as he continued to look on at the ocean, marking the tides.

A Study on the Dwarves

D warves are curious and creative beings, and they are one of the many groupings included within the large collection of species that inhabit Asterra. Known mostly by their tales, which grace many inns and taverns throughout the land, their culture can be traced back millennia, though not as far back as that of the elves or q'zardi. They have a predilection for all things related to mines, smithing, forging, and weaponry. And keeping within the spirit of their crafts, they are often fiery in temper and stricken with conviction. Yet the products of their passionate persona are glorious and unique, and they are what draw many to the dwarves' realm today.

But it is not only what their hands have created that many wish to learn more about. It is the process of such ingenuity, the meticulous methodology of their craft and of their people, which has yielded great halls, raging forges, earth-shattering mines, and wondrous mechanical works, that piques the attention of most folk. The dwarves' kin—the mighty varenijar[2] and nimble gnomes—share many similarities and create many differences. Their enemies—the hjaeti,[3] stone trolls, wicked dryads, cluricauns, and elrime orcs—are vast and vengeful and have been a constant threat throughout time. These allies and villains have added much to people's curiosity about how the dwarven realm came to be. And it is all of this, and much more, which has made the dwarven story more unique than even the wonders found within their mines.

From out of the echoes of the Lost Years there emerged a plethora of dwarven clans, too many to list here but worth exploring another time. Their domain was that of the central span of the Ei' Del River in what is now called modern day Dwathrin. Bound by blood, belief, and kinship, they thrived and expanded for many centuries. Among the many blessings of their new settlements, the dwarves discovered a plethora of ancient paintings and ruins dating from the Lost Years, and with them, they forged their understanding of the world around them. And it was around this time, about three thousand years ago from our present year, 4124 A.L.Y., that the mythos of the dwarves was first believed to have taken form.

Their chief deity, called Fürfir, was the first born in the great Forge of Dæmar from a divine spark. His presence was a glorious light upon the world, but the second born, Gülmirn, was envious of this. Fürfir married Helwig, the third born, and they had a son Dæmar, for which the great forge was named. Their joy was the source of Gülmirn's growing rage, and on a cold night, he kidnapped Dæmar and brought him to his halls in the underworld. And to make sure Fürfir could never claim his son, he had the entrance guarded by Fülwig, the great horned beast, and Turi, the great huntress.

For many years Fürfir and Helwig grieved the loss of their son, and Fürfir grew weak from despair and loneliness. It was then that Helwig gave him the task of creating the world to keep them company. To make sure that Gülmirn would never steal it away from them like he had their son, they entrusted the world's keeping to their greatest chieftain, Reider. Yet the agents of Gülmirn are always lurking in the dark, trying to claim the world for the god of death.[4]

This tale shares some similarities with different stories of creation found among other tribes and peoples within the northeastern region of Asterra. Yet it was the dwarves' story that would see rapid development over the coming centuries. To record these tales and keep their rich traditions alive, the dwarves began the formation of their language, Old Dwarvish,[5] which contains thirty characters and twenty-five letters and can still be heard and seen within the dwarven realm today. This fascinating language and its rapid development brought a more united sense of purpose among the dwarven tribes and clans, and Old Dwarvish soon spread to the varenijar and the gnomes.

Yet, the dwarves' bonds would be tested, and they would, most importantly, be strengthened. For in the latter years of the age of tribes and clans, the dwarven people encountered some of their greatest troubles. To the north and the northwest, the rapacious hjaeti tribes, ruthless elrime orcs, and vile stone trolls also saw a need for rapid expansion, and they set their sights on the Hinderlands, the northern region of modern day Dwathrin and its surrounding areas.

Dwarves are a resilient species, but they were not prepared for the persistent attacks that soon followed. Devastated by war and destruction, the dwarves sought refuge in the mountains and dug great mines within Dwathrin. The varenijar fled to the coasts and fjords of modern day Mikill-Fjörðr, and the gnomes hid within their enchanted woods in the deep recesses of Mirþris-Dún. It was here, for nigh six centuries, that the dwarves and their kin grew in their fondness for their respective environments, and their bodies adapted to the conditions of their surroundings.

In this time the dwarven mines grew deeper, and their metal-lurgy and forging advanced and soon became second nature. They found magic stones within the mines, which they crafted into runic objects to mimic the effects of the magic found within the tales of the old world. However, many of these newly forged runes pulsed with uncontrollable, advanced magical properties beyond the knowledge of even the wisest sages of the time. Internal conflict soon arose among many of the dwarves, who sought the power and knowledge provided by using these magical objects, which quickly led to the use of runes being frowned upon. Yet the dwarven armies grew and their miners delved deeper in an attempt to discover more magical stones and forge more runes. Cities of iron, brass, gold, and silver graced the dwarven mines, creating beacons of light in the dungeons of earth. These were, and still are, some of the oldest dwarven cities in existence. Some, such as Aljamerbaröm-Turöm, which literally means "town of silver" in Old Dwarvish, still stand today.

The dwarves continued to expand, and they soon grew too many for these halls and cities. In this epoch, the dwarven leader, Ruffil Héahart, gathered the dwarves and planned an assault to retake the Hinderlands and the surrounding lands of Dwathrin with the help

of the varenijar from the fjords in the east. Ten years of warfare culminated with the dwarven victory at the Battle of Drut Oil Fields in 2018 A.L.Y., and the hjaeti and other northern peoples were expelled from Dwathrin. Ruffil was named the first king of the dwarves and the city of Héahfæsten was founded in his honor. This would serve as the capital for the first five dwarven dynasties, which now started with Ruffil's reign, the Héahart Dynan.

The Héahart Dynan would last almost three centuries, making it one of the longest of the eight dwarven dynasties of old. To follow were the Dynan Guttern, Uri Dynan, Freya Dynan, Turflin Dynan, Ingrid Dynan, Falxsten Dynan, and Orin Dynan. Over the next millennium, the dwarven realm saw many changes: the Freya Dynan helped save the gnomes from a new series of attacks from cluricaun tricksters in the northeast region of Mirþris-Dún. The Turflin Dynan, under Turflin Guirisson, granted the lands west of the Tempest River and Faerstfell Chasm and east of the Caerulus River to the human empire of Ludus Fen for their aid against the elrime orcs. This pact helped relieve the strain on the dwarven crown in protecting these troublesome lands. And as a result, Ludus Fen was renamed Ohraerandi,[6] in honor of the spirit of the human, dwarven, varenijar, and gnomish alliance.

The dwarves had thrived during these ages of imperial dominance, and their prowess in engineering saw the birth of steam engines and gas engines to benefit their society and their military might. With the discovery of gunpowder in the western realms, the dwarves also soon became the most prolific users of firearms, developing great siege engines and weaponry. But their might turned inward, and the last two dynasties, the Falxsten Dynan and the Orin Dynan, saw much internal conflict and fighting between the dwarves, the varenijar, and the gnomes.

The forbidden use of runes was well documented during these last dynasties. Many saw these runes as a means to end the growing conflict that plagued their realm. With the power of certain runes harnessed, runic spells were more brilliant, sylvan spells were purer, alchemy potions healed better than ever; however, the minds of their users remained unchanged: their goal was only power. Magical forces used to expand imperial might sparked a desire in the occult, and factions developed among different regions and cities. Many denizens of the dwarven realm became corrupted by these magical forces, including many dryads who banded together with cluricauns and other enemies of the dwarves in assailing the realm.

It was not too long after these troubles that the dwarven realm broke into six city-states, and the imperial age of the dwarves came to an abrupt end. These factions—the Gnomish Protectorate, the Sword of Swerðskipvìk, the Fjalcrest Realm, the Kingdom of Héahfæsten, the Kingdom of Isenwíc, and the Norðwur Alliance—battled among each other and also with their human neighbors for over four centuries. This era of great conflict and turmoil is known as the Shattered Years, and it greatly weakened the dwarven realm, causing many dwarves, varenijar, and gnomes to seek refuge in other realms.

In such time, the great dragon Furifveng, seeking to take advantage of the disunity of the dwarven realm, began a series of raids on villages and cities throughout Dwathrin, Mikill-Fjörðr, the Plains of Hildred, and Kuzengard. The realms tried to unite to defeat this threat but failed. It was during the height of turmoil in the Shattered Years when Svensson Burbeard, a great leader of dwarven and varenijar stock, vanquished Furifveng and reunited the six separate realms under the kingdom of Thurgard. Svensson proved himself to be a great leader. And in one of his final valiant acts, he vanquished the evil necromancer Vulmor, who had tried to gain the power of a sacred dwarven rune to control nature. Svensson was celebrated as a legend, and his reign brought much prosperity to the dwarven realm, until he was slain in combat by an assassin loyal to the hjaeti tribes. Svensson is still celebrated today as one of the greatest heroes in dwarven history.[7]

After his passing, his children, Thaid, Thuri, and Ereta, reigned for many years, but the last left no heir; while rule remained stable for the years to follow, it eventually declined, leaving but a council of elders to rule the realm in the stead of a king or queen. Until, after much praise from the people for his repelling of the hjaeti tribes of the north, the governor of Kuzengard, Gælahud[8] Færgut, was crowned king by vote of the people and the council. Gælahud brought economic prosperity back to the dwarven kingdom that Svensson had created and rekindled the fire of dwarven industry. Gælahud had a son, Thayne, who continued his father's legacy. Thayne had a son, Danemere, who is now the current king of the dwarven realm and all of its lands; he is a great and noble king, and he proudly resides in the current capital of Héahfæsten, ever faithful to the lineage, purpose, and history of his people.

The dwarves are a magnificent species, and their ingenuity and perseverance have been a testament to their prosperity throughout the years. Their perseverance has led to large diasporic populations within the central lands and even the deserts of Asterra. Their ingenuity leaves much wonder still to be sought and had for future generations, just as the fire still burns ever brighter in the Forge of Dæmar.

CANDLES OF THE OCHRE HALLS

T homas was born a steadfast adventurer. He remembered this above all else when he first set eyes on the trail of dried blood that carried off into the woods. He could seldom recall what had led him to the far reaches of the cold, desolate wilderness of northeast Ohraerandi. But whatever adventure he had sought now stared at him in velvet tones far richer than his grizzled hair and rugged features could ever hope to embody. And though a weight grew heavy on his legs, he couldn't help but heed the call.

His noble heart beat furiously as he steadily approached and reached down upon the frozen ground. The blood was far more viscous and stranger to the touch than he had imagined; its chilling, curious call led deeper into the forested wilderness ahead where darkness encroached upon the northern lands. And Thomas, ever the inquisitive, empathetic explorer, anxiously followed, hoping to aid whomever or whatever was injured. However, the winter weather had worsened, and he soon lost all but the red path ahead, and when twilight beckoned, the trail all but ended before him. There was not a living soul around; all that stood visible, in the faint distance, was a large stave cathedral atop a lightly forested hill. *Maybe*, he thought to himself, *those within the cathedral might know what happened.*

It was a shaky, uneasy path, but its end was adorned with such a sight. A beautiful ornate gate, which had been mysteriously left open, graced the entrance to welcome Thomas into the small courtyard. The atmosphere was quiet and quaint, filled with forgotten remnants of yesteryear. A large fountain, dry as a bone, lay broken in the center. Shattered mosaic tiles covered the floor beneath it—their weathered and battered images enveloped in weeds. Devoted statues peered from beneath the surrounding cloister, beckoning Thomas ever closer within the grounds. The cathedral door opened without effort, but none were present to greet him save a myriad of wall engravings, enveloping the nave, replete with varying emotions of joy and sadness. Thomas's own confused curiosity joined them, but quickly turned to caution as the rickety, uneven floorboards filled the air with a tumultuous dissonance of disturbance.

He vainly raised his voice. "Hello, is anyone there?" No answer. Again he asked, but silence; and after the third attempt, he got the hint that maybe he shouldn't call out any longer. The long nave of the cathedral proceeded on down to no end. The only light to fill this empty hall was that of candles, which dimly displayed the antiquated woodwork. Their smell led him deeper into the endless void of fleeting light and to an open door and a spiral staircase, leading down to the halls below.

A mindful warning, a desperate, instinctual plea from within, froze him in place, chilling his blood as he looked down into the depths. The darkness brought a reminiscent pain to his mind, and he held his limp left leg as if he relived the trauma that had almost crippled him many years ago. But the curious adventurer in him had come too far to turn back. Down he went, careful at first and then stricken with a sudden sense of haste to remove himself from the twisted enclosure. Far below now, he saw the splendor of the lower halls, far greater than those above. And here he wasn't alone. There were several hooded figures carrying and caring for the candles that lined the halls. They exhibited no awareness of Thomas's presence, save one. This figure was far different from the rest.

The figure approached with a warm smile protruding from the shivering dark. "Hello there, truth seeker, and welcome to the Ochre Halls. What calls you out here in such dark times?"

Thomas's eyes wandered around, still observing the many figures moving aimlessly in the dark. He refocused his gaze on the central figure and gave a faint nod. "I'm Thomas Wilthrow, and I followed a trail of blood through the woods, only to end up here." He peered off again. "Would you or your fellow companions have happened to witness any injured soul? Or happened to see the foulness that caused such pain?"

The figure scoffed lightly and then quickly composed himself. "Wanderer, ease your mind. I believe I speak for my brothers and sisters by saying none of us have seen any troubled being or instance within the surrounding woods. For if so, we would have surely helped them. But in order to uphold our order's manners, I shall have one of my brothers check once the weather clears and the sun shines." He looked towards one of the other hooded figures and, without a word, motioned him away with the gentle sway of his hand. The central figure now slowly turned back to face Thomas. "Speaking of manners, I have been sorely rude." He gently bowed his head. "I am Lucre Moremy, but they call me Father Moremy. Now tell me, what truly was your nature to travel so far east in this barren wilderness of the north? Surely blood is not all that gives impetus to your desire."

Thomas opened his mouth at first, but no words came forth. There was a reluctance, a stutter, but then a calmness. "I am a most seasoned explorer, and I have aided and guided many throughout all of Asterra before I was gravely injured. And though I never lost my desire for adventure, I yearn to find a journey to make me feel whole once more," he said as he took a quick glance at his damaged leg.

"Your leg," Lucre said with a nod. "I could hardly tell from your stance or stride. Your eyes, though, give it away. Your wound"—his voice softened—"you don't seek medicine, you seek absolution for its cause, yes?"

Thomas's forearms grew tense. "Only for its result. I can see it in every passing gaze, and I carry its weight with me every day."

Father Moremy motioned Thomas forward with eagerness. "Then you claim a journey like no other—an adventure to put behind the doubts of the past and reforge yourself anew?" He crept closer; Thomas stood still. "Don't stall with fear. A cleansing pilgrimage, an adventure like no other, is out there, and you found the right sanctuary, Thomas. For I know of more adventure than anyone, and my order is a testament to many feats that can help you leave the past behind and forge yourself anew."

Thomas's eyes couldn't help but wander off and focus on Lucre's devout wardrobe. "But you are simply a priest; a priest of this sanctuary, no?" he said.

Father Moremy laughed lightly. "The treasures and bounties of adventure hide where one least expects them to be, and they similarly are found by those who least likely seem the part. I have seen much that others speak of but never have had the chance to witness: the great clock tower of Zeris, the twilight colors of the Luminous Grove, the mysteries of Mirist Lake, the peak of the Compass Mountains, the depths of the Inverted Cathedral, the mists of the Marshes of Meldaya, and many other wonders. These are the marks of a seasoned adventurer, no?" Thomas needed not reply, for Lucre had his answer frozen in sight. "I can open up your mind to thoughts you never believed were possible. I see the same glimmer of glory, the same desire, in your eyes; am I right, Thomas?"

Thomas broke eye contact and looked away in disbelief. His hairs stood straight on his arms. He was still with caution. But there was something comforting and embracing, though mysteriously veiled, about Lucre's presence. Thomas needed his guidance, and with newfound vigor, he set forth a prayer in the dark. "Yes, I am eager to learn your ways."

Out of the dark, a female hooded figure approached and handed Father Moremy a small burnished red candle, which he lit with an ornate torch. The smell of fleeting wooden embers on a crisp autumn night, fresh pine mixed with rich cedar, filled the air, casting a veil on the candle's third scent—a metallic iron. The scent was accompanied by a reddish ochre hue, which coursed into the depths of the halls.

Father Moremy calmly motioned to the female figure with a wave of his hand. "Gather some food and drink and show Thomas a room, so that he may rest the night and be merry. For tomorrow I shall share my greatest treasures with him." Thomas reluctantly followed the woman and the light she held down the hall. As they walked, she spoke only about her virtuous life within the walls of the sanctuary. But near the end of the hall, she stopped for a moment, staring at the candle she held, and whispered, "Such a beautiful gilded red in this candle. You almost forget you can be burned."

The room he was shown was empty save a small bed, night table, and a tall, dirty mirror. The only light was provided by the faint candle, which the woman quietly placed on the table. From the candle's luminous rays, he could see his reflection in the mirror. His withered, gray, hay-colored hair, his tired eyes, and his rugged, worn leather jerkin, which covered his simple tunic, were the signs of his fruitless adventures but something seemed different to him. This visage before him now was promising.

Thomas reached down, watching his reflection as he cautiously rolled up his pants. He couldn't believe it. The reflection in the mirror showed no scar, and the journey that caused it seemed to slip away from his mind. He could see a brief glimpse of the truth and salvation Father Moremy promised. Thomas smiled as he fixated on the image in the mirror, forgetting the truth, until he grabbed hold of his leg. The scar had never left him, and it returned in the mirror as if the image was only a dream. Now, he remembered the treacherous trail, his companion, and his choice. He couldn't bring back the friend he buried, but he wanted to forget—he needed to forget the pain.

The hooded female figure returned with some food for Thomas. He couldn't think about eating—he felt too tired now—though he entertained the thought, if only to show his gratitude. When she left, he fell asleep quite easily, but it felt as if he hadn't slept but a minute when he awoke the following morning to a strange commotion outside his room.

Father Moremy's eyes were fixed on Thomas from the moment he stepped into the dimly lit halls. "I am afraid there is some bad news, Thomas. It appears an injured man was found in the woods after all."

Thomas's pupils dilated, and his breathing became tiring. "Where is he?"

Father Moremy shook his head and slowly approached Thomas to put his hand on his shoulder. "I am afraid it appears that he succumbed to his wounds during the night."

Thomas put his head down in confusion. "How . . . how did I miss him? I followed the trail right until its end."

"The weather was bad, and it was late, Thomas," Lucre quickly interjected in a calming tone. "You can't blame yourself for this man's death."

Thomas shunned the faint candlelight. His leg pain flared as if the wound was fresh. "I must see him. He should be buried. It would be only right."

Father Moremy nodded calmly. "I understand; go, and when you have finished with the task, return here, and we shall say a prayer."

Thomas left the cathedral, following one of the brothers of the order until they both found the corpse near some brush. Thomas trembled. "I passed by this spot yesterday. There was nothing here." His blood ran as cold as the ice that surrounded the corpse. "I stood here, beholding the sight of the cathedral," he said, as he pointed defiantly towards the ground.

The hooded man seemed unfazed by Thomas's cathartic plea. "It was dark and the weather was poor; you can't blame yourself for not seeing clearly. Let us bury the body and head back to the cathedral." Thomas couldn't remove his eyes from the frozen corpse. He felt his legs would give, just as they did many years ago. But the brother began the task with little care. "Let us not waste any more time; Father Moremy can ease your doubts. He has done so for many before."

They finished burying the body and returned to the cathedral to find Father Moremy in the same position as when they had left him.

He motioned Thomas over. "The burial is complete?"

Thomas simply shook his head in despair.

"Good, then let us say a prayer. And then we can talk more about adventure." He led Thomas and a few of the brothers and sisters into a side room, which contained a grand alter in its center. "Thomas, we shall light a candle in memory. Will that be nice?"

Thomas could only muster one word. "Yes."

"Good." Father Moremy put his head down into his hands and began to mutter indecipherable chants. When he looked up, his eyes were closed, but he soon opened them and greeted Thomas with a smile. He walked over slowly, keeping his hands at his sides. "Thomas, you may not feel like the adventurer you used to be, and this most recent sight could only raise old fears and doubts. But if you trust in me, I can deliver you from this uncertainty. Your adventures can be something new. Do you believe in me, Lucre Moremy, Thomas?"

Thomas nodded. "Yes." In but a moment, Lucre came close to him, almost as if to hug him, but suddenly Thomas felt a cold, sharp pain. It wasn't his leg. He looked down and gazed upon a silver ceremonial dagger drenched in his own blood—his side convulsed in a crimson flow of agony. The wound was not deep, but he felt he could barely move. "What have you done to me?" he cried in anguish.

Father Moremy didn't answer, but called on one of his servants to collect the blood and fatty flesh from the fresh incision and mix it with wax to produce a candle. Thomas saw and remembered the trail of blood that carried off into the woods now vividly in his mind; the viscous scarlet path, a mixture of the same compound used to make this macabre candle. He could see the frozen corpse more vividly than ever. It was just like the one so many years ago, but this time it wasn't an accident; it was more sinister than that: this was murder. He tried to move again, but he had little control over his body as fear crept in from all sides. His thoughts began to crumble and twist, and he was helpless to stop their convulsions and changes.

Father Moremy approached him. "Don't squirm, you will only lose more blood. You should have learned from experience," he said, pointing to Thomas's leg. "It was a horrible accident, so many years ago. Or was it?"

Thomas's mind continued to twist. "The weather was poor; I didn't know the dangers of the trail. I tried to carry him; I tried to save him."

Father Moremy turned his back to Thomas. "You left a bloody trail to where you buried the body."

Thomas shook his head as he furiously closed his eyes, releasing a pool of tears. "I did all I could. How would . . . how would you know what torment it is to dig a friend's grave?"

Lucre writhed forward, facing Thomas again. "I know more than you would like to think, Thomas. You wouldn't believe how many adventurers just like you that I have met. The fellow in the woods wasn't all that different from you at one point. They all have similar tales, but I must admit, you tell your story a bit better than the last few," Lucre said with a smile. "You see, this very cathedral was built as a sanctuary to lost and weary adventurers. Long before I arrived here, a group of pious brothers welcomed in travelers. They used to light candles in the dark and tell tales late into the night."

Father Moremy grabbed one of the nearby candles in the room and held it with admiration. "One night a strange wind blew, and the brothers found their candles would not light. But a newly arrived adventurer presented a candle he had taken from an old, mysterious shrine—a candle whose flame burned as long as they desired. They wished to make their candles last like the one I had brought to their cathedral, so I showed them. The trick is, Thomas, these candles are not lit in memory, they are made of memories. As for you, I have heard the rumors, Thomas; I get around, you know? And lost souls like you are far easier to spot and follow than the rest. You leave a trail, and you'll follow whatever trail is put in front of you in hopes it might lead to your own salvation. You see, I know you far better than you may believe.

"When you finally arrived, I was overjoyed," Lucre continued, as his eyes burned with a reddish hue of ochre vigor. "You were as empty as you made yourself believe, and for that I offered you new adventure and promise, and I have honored my word. I gave you your resolution. No journey was ever your deliverance, and now no journey shall ever be your end. You'll never wander or remember the same path twice till the moment you draw your last breath. Your mind is mine, and it shall twist to my call and my call alone."

Thomas's mind filled with rampant thoughts beyond his grasp, for that in which he had once saw himself a hero, all he could comprehend now was a villain; for his own resolve, he saw cowardice; and a future of promise became one of despair. His mind wandered and raced, creating a new adventure of all he knew and all he would come to know, and he was helpless to change it now.

He watched as Lucre was given the candle containing his blood. A flame flickered in the dark. "Let us light a candle here in memory for you, Thomas." It flickered now in the same pale reddish hue as the others. Father Moremy helped raise Thomas up and handed him the candle to hold. "Now, be a good servant and carry what was once your memory to its place within these somber Ochre Halls."

THE FIRES OF PRESCUS

H iro could still smell the burn and taste the ash from the explosions as the smoke began to lift. He could see the bulwarks and shattered buildings, signaling that he was, in fact, not dead but still alive on the broken streets of Prescus. He took off his helmet to feel the faint wind upon his young, innocent face. His comrades gathered along the bulwarks, regaining their composure, as they anxiously looked into the distance. There was no movement ahead. The surrounding streets were silent. The rustling of a single sheet of paper was the only solemn sound that pierced through the billowing smoke of the dying salvo. "What should I tell my brother in this letter?" Hector said, looking at the rest of the group, his hands still trembling.

"Tell him to ask Ibn to let us forgo this insanely valorous defense," Manius said. "His words might go further than any of ours." The group was silent, with the exception of Myra.

"Maybe just yours, Manius," she said, holding her gaze on the resolute veteran.

"Whatever it is, make it your best; that letter and Hiro's journal might be the only two items to make it out of this city intact," Freida added. Hiro looked away from the front. He was the youngest among them, and his once hopeful face was grim. He joined the Templar Order wishing only to bring change to Asterra and his realm of Verdel, but he never envisioned facing the destructive force and devastation he witnessed over the last several days in Prescus. After being rerouted, his legion had been forced to retreat farther into the tunneled city. There was nowhere for the templar to turn and thus no option left for them but to defend. Prescus was a city carved into the base of the great

Ephesian Range, and it was one of the only safe passageways through the expansive mountains that nearly divided Verdel into two halves. The templar currently held the enemy at a chokepoint, but their forces were gravely outnumbered, and they were dying.

A rogue explosion rippled through the air of the gloomy city, echoing throughout its cavernous sky. Hiro nearly jumped into the fray; the soldiers took cover, peeking their eyes through the crumbled ruins of Prescus, a marred shadow of its former glory, coated in ash. Alessandro, one of the veterans of the group, fixed his eyes on Hiro. "Your timing, Hiro, needs work. Not even a year with the order, and you have found yourself in the midst of its worst conflict in nigh two centuries." A few of the soldiers lightly laughed.

Hiro knew Alessandro well. Alessandro was the first person Hiro had met when he had joined the 17th Legion, and he was the closest thing to a brother he felt he had ever had. Hiro's nerves often made him rigid, but a laugh, even if it was at his own expense, did his mind a bit of good. Hiro looked down at his right hand as he held onto a small trinket he wore around his neck; the patron saint of Verdel was barely visible within his grasp. He composed himself, hoping to add some levity to the situation just as Alessandro had often taught him to do. "There wasn't much to value in my life, so I flipped a coin . . ." There was an awkward silence.

"And?" Alessandro said.

"And I lost hold of it, and it rolled into a sewer; realizing I was now completely broke, I decided to join the templar." Laughter erupted from the group of ten.

A figure approached them. It was the centurion, this battered century's noble commander, Ibn Abdel. "They'll keep firing if you keep talking." There was immediate silence. "There will be plenty to laugh about once we all make it out of here."

The group of ten looked at each other, their faces ash among the rubble under the great mountain. "We were a century still eighty strong but a few days ago," Hector said.

Myra leaned up against the bulwark and let out a deep breath. "And once a legion before that."

"And Verdel is still a kingdom as long as we hold this bastion," Ibn remarked. "We are still a century, a legion."

Manius quickly looked away from the front to face Ibn. "We can't hold Prescus much longer, Ibn, not in this condition. The esterelians are vicious, worse than the orcs; they spare no one, and they and their allies outnumber us. Let them have this city; we can regroup, and then hold their advance past the Ephesian Range."

Ibn gave him a stern look. "The wounded won't make it out of this city with us, Manius. And we would be leaving not only them behind but every soul that has fought for Prescus." He pointed towards a group of nine rugged and war-torn defenders of Prescus from the Crown of Verdel farther down the bulwark. "You would offer the enemy their spirits along with over two-thousand years of our tradition?"[9]

Manius dropped his head in silence. Ibn looked at the rest of them and then turned his back towards the great stone gateway leading out from under the mountain. "If they take Prescus, they will gain a foothold out west, and we won't contain them in the open, not with our numbers. Every moment that passes, reinforcements come to relieve Prescus from the north. This is the only safe passageway through these mountains, besides a two-day travel north. The enemy knows this, and so do we. A templar always finds something to defend and a purpose to hold onto: it is our oath. We will defend Prescus even during its grimmest hour."

Hiro peered over his shoulder and saw the look of the battered remaining group of soldiers fighting under the Crown of Verdel. They posted guard near a broken, yet still standing, statue of the same patron saint of Verdel that dangled from his neck: Illian Pelinar.

The second in command, Danilo Auleus, grimly approached. He pulled Ibn aside. "Our supplies are dwindling; we have not enough to treat the growing number of wounded, and our empyrean magic can only go so far."

Ibn gave Danilo a curious, concerned look. "Our healing incantations are some of the strongest in the whole 17th Legion. Have we lost all ability to take care of our own?"

"We have few experienced healers left, and they operate with little time, concentration, or energy," Danilo said.

"Any word on Alrisa, Talriq, or any of the others?"

Danilo shook his head solemnly. "No, but the enemy holds all of Prescus to this point, and they do not keep prisoners, Ibn."

Ibn gave a heavy sigh. "We keep searching for them, no matter what. The enemy's advance has been held since the sixth night of the siege. We might be able to send a few more sorties out before they regroup, and we can also try to salvage some of the supplies left in Prescus. Henry is running late, but hopefully he returns with good news on our situation."

Hiro looked down the grim streets ahead, moving closer to the edge of the makeshift bulwark that spanned the end of the bombed-out street the templar had chosen to defend. The rest of his comrades stayed put in their positions. Freida and Alessandro conversed over a pile of rubble from the barely standing tavern that had once proudly stood on the corner. Manius tried to ease Hector's nerves by sharing a conversation and a bit of his rations. The rest of the templar were still.

Hiro could feel his own nerves begin to weaken his stance. His body was withered, but he mustered his energy and stood resolute as he faded into thought. He resumed walking slowly ahead.

"Hiro, don't get too adventurous," Freida said.

He locked his gaze forward. "Shouldn't the others have returned by now?"

A few of them peered out to look ahead. There was no one in sight.

"Maybe Henry found the others," Freida said hopefully.

Myra wasn't nearly as hopeful. "He's probably rummaging around for a few souvenirs."

Manius laughed. "He'll never get his fill. I know just how he thinks."

Explosions and the sound of running suddenly echoed throughout the streets. Hiro took cover along with the rest of the troops. Ibn saw faint figures running down the desecrated, winding alleyways. It was Corinna and Valens, returning from their patrol, holding up a wounded Henry as they ran from the impending danger that lurked ever closer.

"To attention, templar. Consecrate your weapons with your holy magic. Cover them," Ibn shouted in Altirtung, the language of the templar. "Attendite, templarī. Tēla tua cum magicā arte sanctā tuā sancīte. Tegite ea"[10] was all the enemy would be able to hear. Ibn motioned to a small artillery detachment behind them, still containing two light ballistae; they fired special smoke bolts to mask the returning templar's route from the enemy.

Hiro grabbed his composite bow. He aimed down its sight; the enemies, though, stopped their pursuit, safely looking on from a distance as the smoke began to cover the returning templar as they moved behind the cover of the bulwark. "Where is he hurt?" Hiro said, fixating on Henry's dazed and bloodied state.

"Just keep your focus and eyes forward," Valens said. Hiro couldn't look away. He barely held his bow steady as the smoke cleared. Nothing had changed; the enemy didn't move. They surely had sent their message: for now, the templar army would continue to bleed and starve.

Corinna and Valens exchanged a few, brief words with Ibn as Henry faded in and out of consciousness. "Get him into the townhall. Have Sasha treat him," Ibn said quickly. He looked down at Henry. He put his hand on Henry's head and moved his hair back. "We will see you through this, brother. Stay strong." Corinna and Valens carried Henry off. Both sides of the perimeter were silent—ten souls guarding the southern half of the great stone passageway out west, sixteen souls guarding the north, and the artillery behind them.

Ibn covered his chin with his hand as he watched Henry disappear into the townhall. He pulled Danilo aside. They whispered among themselves. "They found Alrisa and the others; they didn't make it. We are but thirty-seven now, including Sasha and the two combat medics." He clasped his sword, lying in its scabbard. "We should have known that this reckless fighting wouldn't stay contained within the central realms. The Crown of Verdel acted valiantly but impulsively in coming to Magris' aid. We were already too late upon our arrival. The Trifex Alliance has only grown stronger in the passing weeks. If we lose Prescus, they will march westward to Balgra, and the realm

of Verdel will surely capitulate under such pressure. Only a few more blocks of city for them to cross the Ephesian Range."

Ibn looked up at the towering stone sky, illuminated by great cauldrons of flame hanging throughout the mountain's core. Behind him, the end of Prescus West was glossed by the encroaching rays of the unnerving moon from the open world.

He returned his attention to Danilo. "Have we received new word from Legio Atlatica?"

"The last message was carried by the messenger bird yesterday afternoon—none from that point on."

Ibn shook his head. "Danilo, make sure the troops use no empyrean incantations outdoors through the night. Keep them vigilant, keep them strong. I will meet with Sasha, and check our supply situation." The two quickly parted.

Near the front, Hiro could hear the breeze whistling through the great western passage of the mountain. It was so close: the free open world, right behind him; the one he had willingly left behind. He wrote down a few passages in his journal, keeping it close to his side, as he gazed off into the distant world.

"Hiro," a voice called, "are you daydreaming again?"

He put away his journal and shook himself to attention. "Can it be so if it is night?" he said, as he quickly turned around; it was Alessandro, who greeted him with a light smirk.

"You got stuck on patrol for the evening, or are you just catching some fresh air?"

"Thankfully the latter. But I doubt there is much fresh air left in this enclosed city—mostly smoke and ash." Hiro looked ahead at the crumbled buildings—their debris lined the streets leading up to the templar bulwarks.

"You'll get used to it in time; it builds character."

Hiro gave a small smirk of his own. "I never can remember, how long have you been a part of the order?"

"I'm that old to you, ey?" Alessandro said with a small laugh. "Unfortunately, not long enough to be able to get away from missions such as these, but just enough time to be able to tolerate them to an extent." He took a deep sigh. "Nine years, Hiro, and I would like to believe that every day made a difference here in Asterra."

"And after all that good, still so much trouble?" Hiro gazed in a trance of confusion.

"Disappointed?"

"Just unsure."

"Of what?"

Hiro looked down. "That is what I am unsure about."

Alessandro laughed. "Well, we aren't going anywhere, so there is plenty of time to figure out just why you are here."

The streets were empty, filled only with silence; the encroaching solitude was an unwelcome visitor, but Hiro knew better now than to turn it away for the time being. It wasn't meant to last.

An explosion rang out into the night, reverberating off the mountainous dome of the city. The ballistae were manned by their crews, and the bulwarks were fortified with the presence of the ardent templar and soldiers of Verdel. The sound of impending commotion indicated that an army approached. Subtlety was rightly abandoned by the brazen force of the enemy that had been now regained.

"To your positions," Ibn said. He looked towards the front. "Conserve arrows, lest your magic is strong enough to emblazon their bite; their armor is far too heavy."

Hiro could see them. Esterelian brutes, humanoid-like dragons, clad in piles of steel led the first wave of orcs and humans through the street, across roughly three-hundred meters of the templar front. Crude weapons of fire and sulfur erupted, hitting the bulwarks as the approaching wave bore forth their swords and shields. Crude horns sounded throughout the marred city.

The templar stood resolute along the front. A few emblazoned arrows were set lose, striking down their targets in a blaze of light. Hiro could see a few of his comrades conjuring a bit of their empyrean incantations, casting shimmers of light to meet the chaotic fire in the darkness. Hiro's magic was still weak but effective enough. He placed his confidence in his bow, and he used it with all the strength and courage he could muster. In a fury, when the gap of the fray enclosed upon his position, he set loose upon the enemy with his sword. Vindicating steel, emblazoned by a modicum of empyrean spark from his training, set heavy his hand. His will was the only force stronger than its bite.

Hiro reassured himself that he would not fall here; even when tossed aside by one of the brutes, he quickly regained his composure and struck the beast down with a vengeance. He would not abandon his duty; he had to defend his comrades. Yet, it was not until the sounds of battle subsided that he realized how few still stood among them.

He thought himself lucky to be unharmed, but the silence brought about the loudest cries, which pierced through the night. He remembered empyrean healing magic best from his training. He could see the ground littered with the battered bodies of his friends. Nearest to him, someone tried to crawl back to the safety of the bulwark, still in shock. It was Hector, his body far too broken to move any farther. Hiro knelt beside him; he called out for aid, but he knew there were far too many wounded to wait for more help to arrive. He fuddled through what little supplies he had and tried to concentrate on casting his healing magic, but he was too nervous. His hands were shaking, but he tried again. This time it worked; he could see the blinding purity of the magic mixed with water to heal and clean the wounds and bandages to cover them.

He thought he could save Hector. He felt that his fellow brother, Hector, was at least calming down. Hector looked at Hiro, experiencing a respite from the pain. His eyes closed. Hiro was still. He looked down at Hector; one of them was at peace. Hiro stared at his hands in disbelief—in disappointment. There was no deliverance from this pain. An old wound was reborn in Hiro's heart. He was another casualty on the streets of Prescus.

"Hiro," a voice called. "Hiro," it said again. "Are you wounded?"

He was reluctant to turn around. "No, but Hector . . ." He stumbled on his words. His face was pale. "I couldn't help him."

Alessandro helped him up from the ground. "You did what you could, Hiro. You need to focus on what is left here to defend—for

Hector and for the rest of the fallen. We have more wounded, and they need aid."

Hiro followed Alessandro, but his mind was left on the front. He could here Ibn talking in the distance. "How many left to fight?" Ibn faintly said.

"Eighteen, not counting Sasha, Nidra, and Arcturo," Danilo replied. "There are only three fighters from the Crown of Verdel left. Shall they die here? We should let them go, Ibn. Let them stand with us only if they want."

Ibn looked towards the three soldiers as they gathered their dead. They had no intention of leaving their city or their fallen behind.

The following day was scattered with the sounds of intermittent artillery fire. The enemy was closing its grasp upon the templar position. Ibn motioned to the western passage out of Prescus. "Ready another messenger bird. Legio Atlatica must quicken their pace." As the message was sent off to the heavens, another word traveled among the remaining defenders—reinforcements wouldn't arrive in time.

Hiro could see another night setting in as the sun retreated from Prescus West. The intermittent explosions ceased. The cauldrons of fire burned above. The townhall, the only sign of life behind the desolate bulwarks, sent out faint rays of light from the clutches of the impending closure of its entranceway. "How is Henry?" he asked of Alessandro.

Alessandro paused momentarily. He let out a staggered breath. "He passed last night, Hiro."

Hiro nervously fidgeted with his trinket. He compulsively reached for his journal but let his hand fall to his side. "He often talked to me about his farm in Aurora." He looked away. "Was there anything we could have done?"

Alessandro shook his head. "No, I don't believe there was, Hiro." He looked at the rest of the troops and then back to Hiro. "Was what you said a few days ago, about joining the order, true?"

Hiro looked at Alessandro. "Yes, all except for the part with the coin."

Alessandro nodded. "That bad, huh?"

"Just different. I was born in a province not too far from here. I don't remember it as well as I should." He shook his head lightly, and looked down at his trinket. His hands were shaking. "I only have a few memories." He nervously smirked. "I was found in a bad part of a bad town. Abandoned by many without cause, until the day I was found by a soul with more to give. I still had my troubles, but some wouldn't leave me behind no matter what. I was given this trinket as a reminder that no matter how lost you feel, there is always someone waiting for the day you are found."

He looked Alessandro in the eyes. "I thought I could repay the same kindness to Asterra that was bestowed upon me, starting with the realm of my birth. The light of the templar offered purpose." Hiro turned his gaze to the fires throughout Prescus. "But it seems no matter the effort, the world always has a way of reverting itself back to chaos."

"You aren't the personality I often come across on a battlefield," Alessandro said. "You'll blind yourself with that belief about the holy light, and you'll see worse than if you were in the dark. Whether there is a purpose for us being right here, right now or not is irrelevant; you create your own mission and purpose; neither the world nor the light supply it."

A great boulder smashed into one of the buildings nearby followed by a few small explosions. Hiro saw Ibn rallying the defenders.

"Have the bulwarks manned; they don't plan to let us see another night. But they will not pass through Prescus as long as this line holds. This is your bastion," Ibn said to all of them. "What might drive their army forward is not here for the taking, for it is already owned by you, and it is never to be taken by whatever force opposes you. It is yours to keep, as this is your line to hold."

Hiro stood with the rest of the defenders at the front of the bulwarks, awaiting the impending advance of the enemy. He could see the smoke rising; flames of the enemy signaled the hordes forward. "What leaves this tomb alive?" he mumbled to himself.

The silence broke; the streets erupted with the sounds of destruction. The templar held their position. They were the far superior fighters in close-quarter combat, but they couldn't hold off the mass of enemies that were advancing upon their position. The lines were breaking; the cries to bolster the formations were silenced, engulfed in the screams of battle.

"To the townhall. Leave none behind," Ibn shouted, frantically motioning the remaining few to pull back. A templar fell; the last fighter from the Crown of Verdel was lost to the fray. The ballistae fired to cover the few retreating, but a mass of enemy artillery returned fire. One of the ballistae and its crew were engulfed in flames. More projectiles followed; the townhall was hit. Ibn looked onward in disbelief as the roof caved in, and the building was set ablaze.

Hiro ran to pick up Valens, who had been injured, but a cannon had them in its sight. Alessandro saw this and ran to push them both out of the way. But he only made it to Hiro before the explosion hit the ground, tossing Valens and Alessandro chaotically aside. When Hiro found them, Valens was gone and Alessandro was in a great deal of pain.

Hiro attempted to carry Alessandro away, so that he could treat his wounds from the safety of cover. But Alessandro wearily lifted his hand and put it on Hiro's arm. He was trembling in shock but regained his composure for a moment. "It was an honor, Hiro, but you still need to work on your timing, brother," he said with a faint smile, before succumbing to his wounds.

Hiro panicked as he held Alessandro's lifeless body. "Alessandro? Alessandro!" he shouted in vain. He carried him away behind the last line of defenses and closed Alessandro's eyes. Hiro looked around. Fires burned everywhere; a few templar stood left, including Ibn and Myra and a few others. Danilo was being treated by Manius. In a blaze of vicious light, sulfur filled the air; Manius fell to the ground. Myra and Ibn soon followed. Hiro went to pick up Danilo as the enemy approached.

"Defend yourself, Hiro, hold Prescus for as long as you can." Danilo waved Hiro away, as he mustered his remaining strength to prop his body against the rubble and face the enemy. Danilo concentrated and conjured his empyrean magic. A blaze of light emitted from his hand, striking down the first enemy. He emblazoned his shield and deflected the force from another enemy, striking him dead too. He turned to face a storming orc, but he was felled by the swift blow of an esterelian brute's massive sword. Hiro, despite his best efforts, was all alone to defend Prescus from the impending chaotic swarm of the enemy's advance.

He could see them celebrating as they overran the templar's position. "What can I do against such an army as this?" Hiro painfully whispered to himself, beholding the sight of his dead comrades. "What fight have I left to oppose them?" They tore down the statue of Illian Pelinar; they desecrated his fallen brothers and sisters. There was nothing left to hold onto but himself and his mission; engulfed in a void of flames, Hiro stood in the ruthless streets of Prescus, and remembered his oath: *what is lost to the world, a templar always finds, for there is always something to defend and a purpose to hold onto.*

Nigh two days he held out in the city, ardently holding onto the will of the 17th Legion. He rummaged through the rubble for any means to prolong the enemy's advance. He found a hidden stash of gunpowder used by resistance fighters in the city, and it soon became his only companion. Using what little empyrean magic he could muster, he set ablaze the containers he had placed strategically among the torn structures of Prescus West. Falling rubble crushed the enemy formation, and they halted their advance to regroup.

They cautiously moved forward again through the limits of Prescus. Hiro used the gunpowder to the last ounce, and when it was finished, he met the enemy only with a purpose to defend his ground. He fought valiantly until a mighty blow struck him down; he clutched his pendant, his diary dropping to the floor. The world turned dark around him as the troops marched over his dying body. Formless chaos seemed to embrace his body as his last breath left him. The last defender of Prescus fell.

The enemy had claimed Prescus, but their cheers were quickly deafened. Valiant horns sounded from afar; they came from Prescus East, the great entrance of the city opposite to where the enemy was positioned. Legio Atlatica had arrived, wielding the vindicating justice of the Templar Order. They quickly cut through the enemy's ranks and drove them from Prescus to search desperately for fleeting hope until their inevitable reckoning.

On the clearing battlefield, the commander, Quintus Amaris, found the bodies of the brave defenders of Prescus. There was Alessandro, Ibn, Myra, Valens, Hector, and all of the others.

They found Hiro's lifeless body and his journal. His pendant was somewhere else though. A young girl had retrieved it from a fallen enemy who had stolen it from Hiro's body. She had hid in the rubble, among the hopeless streets, praying the darkness would go away. Her hope was near depleted as she heard the enemy advance through the city, ever closer to her hiding spot. All she could do was continue to pray they didn't find her, for who could save a child lost in the fires of this ruined city? Who could believe she existed there at all among the flames?

Now, Quintus went to the young girl. She was weak, but her spirit was strong. He asked her name, and she faintly responded, "Medriel."

He knelt down before her and smiled. He saw the battered pendant dangling from her neck, which still managed to maintain its shine despite the apparent scars of battle. "What a beautiful pendant you have there, Medriel. Is it yours?"

She shook her head. "No, I found it in the city."

Quintus smiled. "Only someone who was once lost carries a pendant of Illian Pelinar. Medriel, for each soul that was here, to them, you were always destined to be found."

THE CULT OF PALDERMEN

There are some places in Asterra that parents tell their children to never wander. Parson's Fold, nestled within the plains of Middrit, conjures more than the occasional cautionary tale whose truth is hidden well within the village's hollow welcome. But these stories were not always so prominent, not for Elmyra Jansson and Gerlad Holfer, two clerics who had embarked on a noble mission from Solemn Vow Abbey in the realm of Ohraerandi to spread peace and the call of the light to the once war-torn regions of the central realms.

Their destination was Emervell, a busy trading town in northern Middrit. Alas, the roads of the sprawling steppes within the central realms were poorly marked, and they had lost their way along the selected route and now found themselves cluelessly searching for a means to right their course. With daylight fading, an ominous gray veil descended upon the golden steppes, but the two brave clerics were determined to fulfill their quest. They mustered their concentration, only for it to be broken when a young maiden suddenly appeared from the brush on the opposite side of the road. She was crying profusely and could barely catch her breath.

She stopped before them, desperately trying to regain a semblance of composure. "Oh, please, hither forth. I was assailed by a thief." The woman winced in pain as she showed her left side, which was bloodied and bruised.

Elmyra, showing her benevolent nature, quickly ran over to the young woman. "Are you hurt elsewhere?" she said, quickly tending to the lady's wounds.

Gerlad looked around, standing guard with his large frame set against the distant darkening sky. "Which way did the thief go?" he said.

"I am not sure. I was on my way to Carden Cottages near Parson's Fold when I was attacked from the side. It happened so quickly, but his face has been a haunting visage that seems to last forever." She took a heavy breath and grabbed ahold of Elmyra's left shoulder, just under the collar line, in a moment of weakness. "He slashed me at the side and stole my money and goods and was off. He must be far gone by now. I was foolish to travel alone so late in the day." She whimpered. "How will I get to Carden Cottages in this condition?" she said, desperately trying to hold back her tears.

Elmyra finished healing her wounds with her empyrean magic and medicine and warmly embraced the young woman. "Don't worry, we shall accompany you on your journey to Carden Cottages. Our magic isn't just for healing," Elmyra said with a comforting smile.

The lady almost broke down in tears, yet her pain was nigh gone. "What blessed souls you both are. You are a true light to be found."

The sun had near set when they arrived at Carden Cottages. The young woman approached her small home and gave the two a warm wave goodbye, examining their faces, which were joined only among the dark silhouetted hills. She stood within the parting light of her cottage's doorway. "I had a feeling you two were lost from the moment I first saw you. I would take you in, but my husband does not take kindly to strangers, even those that are well-mannered. But Parson's Fold is within an hour's walk from here. When you arrive, go to the Mercy Haven Inn; ask for Mrs. Tilly Duvell. Tell her Bethel Ager sent you."

They thanked Bethel and followed the road to their new destination. "Parson's Fold, I have never heard of such a place," Elmyra said with a curious look towards Gerlad.

He met her with the same look. "Yes, it didn't seem to be on the map. It could have been left out. But it sounds rather promising, and what other choice do we have?"

She looked at her book of incantations and then continued forward, looking back for a brief moment at the last rays of the fleeting sun. "I suppose you are right, Gerlad. I just hope we won't be late to Emervell; we have much work to do, and every moment is a good deed wasted."

"Well, I believe you have brought about one this evening, and put an end to what has been a dismal start to a promising journey," Gerlad said. Elmyra smiled as they headed into the dark night.

When they arrived in Parson's Fold, it wasn't difficult to find the Mercy Haven Inn; it was the only inn in town, and the weathered sign heralded its excellence, which was emphatically repeated by the owner, Mrs. Tilly Duvell.

Elmyra gave a warm welcome as she approached the desk. "Do you have any rooms available for two for the night? We were recommended this inn by Mrs. Bethel Ager."

Mrs. Tilly smiled widely. "Oh, what a wondrous surprise. How is Bethel?"

Gerlad awkwardly contorted his face, not knowing what to say at first. "She was assailed by a thief, but we have healed her of her wounds and accompanied her home."

Mrs. Tilly gave a sudden, short gasp. "By the sands of Xirtis, why would someone do such evil to an innocent soul like Bethel?" She shook her head in a defiant bout but then quickly regained her composure. "Well, at least there are still good souls in this world, and she sent them unto us for good fortune," she said with an amicable gaze at Elmyra and Gerlad. "Now, for those rooms, I will be more than happy to accommodate you. And the cost is on the house for assisting our dear Bethel—but just for one night?" She examined them both with her wandering eyes. "You two look as if you haven't had a good night's sleep or a good meal in days."

Gerlad's eyes illuminated with a bit of vigor. "It has been a long journey for us," he said.

Before Elmyra could rebuttal with a proclamation of their mission, Mrs. Tilly interjected. "We sure do love having travelers visit Parson's Fold. Where might you two be from?"

Elmyra smiled amicably. "We are from Ohraerandi."

Mrs. Tilly joined her hands in gratitude. "Ah, you must know of the stories of the templar knights, yes? Such fascinating work they do."

"We do, and we also share a bit of their mission, though without the overzealous authority," Gerlad said proudly.

"Well, all friends of the light are welcome here. You may deliver us proudly from any and all sorrows. But that shall have to wait till the morning, ey?" she said, looking at the two tired travelers.

Gerlad and Elmyra made little rebuttal and quickly went to their respective bedrooms to sleep. Elmyra gave Gerlad a wave goodnight across the abandoned hallway. "Remember that we are still due in Emervell, so we must find directions in the morning and be on our way."

Gerlad wished to indulge a sigh but held it in. "We should at least have a good meal before we hit the road again."

Elmyra laughed. "Of course, now let us get some sleep." There was little to think about for the tired duo before they were quickly asleep, finally able to rest their weary bodies. But as they slept, a crowd gathered outside, and the commotion soon stirred them awake in the early hours of the morning.

"What else did they take?" one of the voices said loudly for all to hear.

"What did they leave is surely a better thing to ask," a frail voice said with a cry. A small lady stood out from the crowd. "They took the myrrh, the frankincense, and almost every valuable fragrance." The lady burst into tears; she was the owner of a small shop that purveyed many valuable scents from all over Asterra.

"Why would someone steal such items?" one of the villagers said.

"Do thieves ever think of what they steal? They only care about how much they can sell the goods for. I gather the price per pound was easy enough for a traveling thief."

"But what thief comes to steal in a small backwater town such as Parson's Fold?" another voice shouted.

Having walked outside with Gerlad upon first hearing the crowd, Elmyra stepped forward almost immediately. "A lady, a Mrs. Bethel

Ager, was assailed by a thief on our way to town just yesterday."

The townsfolk turned towards Elmyra and Gerlad almost in unison. "Who might you be?" an inquisitive voice beckoned.

"Two clerics and defenders of the light who are anxious to help remedy your plight," Elmyra said. "And I am sure Bethel can help identify this thief, as it is probably the same person who robbed her."

There was a growing confusion among the gathering crowd. "Who is this Bethel that you ask us to place our hopes in? I have never heard of such a person." A few other folks nodded in agreement.

Elmyra immediately thought of Mrs. Tilly; she knew Bethel and could tell them who she was. However, when Elmyra and Gerlad went back into the inn, Mrs. Tilly was nowhere to be found.

Elmyra was determined in her pursuit of justice, though. "I can lead you to Bethel; she has at least seen the face of the thief that attacked her. Maybe we might find the perpetrator yet."

"This is just a distraction," an angry voice proclaimed.

"Nonsense at its best; a diversion at its worst," another voice added as the crowd grew with tension and a clamoring tide.

But there was a calm parting: one among the crowd approached Elmyra. It was a small woman, who walked forward with unmistakable resolve and poise. Her short, dark brown hair covered a bit of her stern looking face, but she had a concerned look in her eyes. She was one of the few among the crowd that wanted to help. Her name was Ruthanne Nolta; the townsfolk called her Ruthie, and she was the marshal of Parson's Fold. Her rustic attire and simple appearance could hardly confirm her rank, but a small emblem on her denim shirt gave Elmyra all the info she needed. "I will follow you there come sunrise. Why should we not seek answers?" she beckoned, looking back at the crowd of her neighbors. A few of them grumbled.

But the butcher, Mr. Hiato Akashi, knew Ruthie well. He stepped forward. "Yes, you would think more would support any and all means to find the perpetrator," he said, looking at his fellow citizens with a disappointed gaze. "If you lead the investigation, Ruthie, I shall stand behind it." Only a few stood with him; the rest thought little of such futility.

When Elmyra, Gerlad, and Ruthanne entered Carden Cottages in the morning, they approached the same house from the night before. They knocked at the door once, but there was no answer. A second time, nothing. Then a third, when in a bout of concern, Gerlad broke through the door. All three of their faces were riddled with confusion.

The house, well, no one could have lived in such a place in at least twenty years. There were cobwebs and inches of dust caked on each piece of furniture. The floorboards creaked with every step, and mold had claimed this dwelling as its own.

Elmyra stuttered, looking at Ruthanne, desperately forcing the words to come out of her mouth. "This was the place where we dropped her off . . . I know it." She looked at Gerlad for reassurance.

He nodded, but his eyes wandered, unsure of their surroundings. "Maybe we were mistaken."

"No, Gerlad, I saw her approach the door and open it to embrace a warm light."

"Did you happen to see inside the house?" Ruthanne inquired.

"No, I did not. We parted ways after she told us of the Mercy Haven Inn and of Mrs. Tilly. She said her husband wouldn't take in visitors." Her lips quivered with uncertainty.

"Well, then there is nothing left for us to do then but to return to town and try to find Mrs. Tilly," Ruthie said, as she concluded her search of the acrid, gloomy house. Elmyra and Gerlad had no choice but to follow.

When the three of them returned to Parson's Fold, it was peak morning, and most of the townsfolk had continued on with their affairs as if nothing had occurred earlier that morning. Ruthie, along with Elmyra and Gerlad, though, went looking for Mrs. Tilly, but were unsuccessful.

Gerlad turned to Elmyra. "It seems unlikely for someone to leave a whole hotel unmanned. But then again, we seem to be its only guests."

"Yes, it is odd, but what hasn't been since we stepped within this town?" Elmyra said. "While Ruthie goes asking questions around town, I am going to get a bit of rest. I don't believe we will be getting the answers we seek anytime soon."

Gerlad didn't argue a bit. He was the first up the stairs and quickly entered his room. Elmyra, though, seemed to carry a burden with each step and opened her door lethargically. And there, where she thought she might finally gain a semblance of composure, she found Mrs. Tilly with a look of pain and a contortion of confusion visible on her face. She had been dismembered into pieces that were spread all over the room. Elmyra screamed and crumbled to the floor in horror. Gerlad wasted little time running across the hallway to find Elmyra up against the wall, eyes wide open, staring at the scarlet macabre sight before them.

"Is . . . is that Mrs. Tilly," Gerlad said with a cold tremor.

Elmyra was crying; she couldn't hold in her tears. In what felt like many years, she couldn't conjure but an iota of light within her. "What do we do?" she said in a cathartic burst of agony. She ran her hands through her short red hair and held her head down against her knees.

Gerlad laid his large hand on her shoulder. "I'll go get Ruthie."

When Gerlad returned with Ruthie, there was little to be said. Ruthie was in just as much shock as them.

"How long do you think she has been like this?" Gerlad asked.

Ruthie looked at the scarlet stains. "The blood is dry. She has been here for a while. When did you arrive in Parson's Fold?"

"Yesterday evening," Gerlad quickly answered.

"Was there anyone else in the tavern when you checked in?"

"I don't believe so; it was quiet, and it has been that way since."

Ruthie took a look around the room. She stopped in her tracks.

Elmyra was curled up in a ball on the floor. Gerlad slowly approached Ruthie, his eyes fixed ahead. "What is it?"

"A message, written in blood."

"What type of message?"

"Come here and see it for yourself." Ruthie stepped aside.

Every letter came into view, one right after the other. It was clear; it was short: *Avert thine eyes and hear me cry.*

"Who would do something like this?" Gerlad stammered. "Surely only a daemon could have such disregard for life."

"Daemon or not, this village, especially this inn, is not safe. I will alert the rest of the villagers. Follow me. I will find another place where you both can stay for now, until we are able to gather some more information."

Alas, there was little progress made in the following days, and the townsfolk grew more restless. They started by accusing each other, but most soon began to point their fingers at Elmyra. Surely she must have had some hand in the matter if the body was found in her room. But why would a cleric like Elmyra wish to cause harm to a lady she had just met? Most importantly, were the murder and the robberies committed by the same fiendish being?

Ruthie began to have her own suspicions as well. A curious thought came to her when she first went to view the spot where the supposed Mrs. Ager was assailed. The blood near the brush was present and dry, but every branch, every bush, even down to the last bud, seemed to be intact, barely moved. Ruthie was perplexed: there was no doubt an attack. But a struggle? Something didn't seem right.

She returned to town to find Elmyra all alone and Gerlad nowhere to be found. When prompted on his whereabouts, Elmyra gave a faint turn of her head. "He said he was going to get some provisions from the general store only but a few minutes ago. He should return within the hour."

"I walked through town to get here and passed the general store. Foolish of me I didn't think to look inside, but it didn't seem like there were any customers." Ruthie motioned Elmyra up and gave her a hand to help her to her feet. "Maybe we can go look for Gerlad together? I have some important news that I would like to share with you both."

Elmyra took a few burdensome steps forward. "Are you alright?" Ruthie said.

"I have this pain in my upper back and shoulders; I first thought it might be the way I slept, but it has started to burn."

Ruthie slowly walked over and moved Elmyra's collar down to reveal a blood-red rash. "My word, how did you come by this?"

Elmyra appeared to be getting more fevered. "I can't recall, but I remember talking to Gerlad about how we couldn't find Parson's Fold on our map. Strange, isn't it? Why would it be so?" she said dazedly.

"I think you should rest while I go search for Gerlad."

Elmyra raised her hand in a sudden burst of newfound vigor. "No, no, I can make it. I am hoping to walk out of this town. Maybe it has been left off the map for a reason. Might you know?" she asked again in her state of confusion.

Ruthie indulged the request this time. "Parson's Fold was a town born after the great war by a group of folks seeking only deliverance from the terrors they had witnessed. Besides it being relatively new, I wouldn't know why it wouldn't be on your map." Elmyra didn't answer. She seemed to have forgotten the question she had asked.

They entered the center of town and soon heard Gerlad shout. He was running towards them. "I found the assailant," he cried aloud. "We might be able to catch him together; he can't escape us all," he said in a frenzy. Ruthie ran, following Gerlad, unknowingly leaving behind Elmyra who had grown more lethargic with each motion forward.

"Gerlad, ease up," Ruthie said, looking back and finding no sight of Elmyra. "Where did you find the suspect?"

Gerlad took a moment to catch his breath. "I was just leaving the general store when I witnessed someone trying to break into the blacksmith's shop. I ran after the figure, trying my best to keep pace. I followed the trail all throughout town, but I couldn't keep up any longer. I decided to make my way back to Elmyra, and then that's when I ran into you both."

"Speaking of Elmyra, we ought to get back and find her. She didn't look well today."

A few moments later, there were screams emanating from down one of the secluded side alleys. They quickly followed the noise and arrived to witness a fire within the butcher's store. Elmyra was nearby on the ground, having been unable to keep her balance.

"What happened here?" Ruthie said. "Where is Mr. Akashi?" She ran to the front of the burning building, ready to run inside to save her dear friend, but Gerlad stopped her. The building was engulfed in an inferno of fiendish flames.

"We have to save him," she cried in a desperate plea, but Gerlad knew there was nothing either of them could do.

Once the flames settled, the townsfolk gathered around the charred building, and all they could surmise was that this, just like the other incidents, was the work of Elmyra. Mr. Akashi's body was found burned, but there appeared to be bruises hidden under the seared flesh as well. Ruthie knew that there was something wrong with Elmyra and Gerlad's story, but she couldn't see either of them committing any of these crimes. She wasted little time in escorting them both to safety, as it appeared the townsfolk were growing into a frenzy.

Ruthie sat Elmyra and Gerlad down. "I went to the supposed place that you had described finding this Bethel Ager. You never saw the assailant, correct?"

Elmyra and Gerlad shook their heads in unison. "No, why?" Gerlad said. Elmyra seemed detached from the situation at hand.

"I have never seen the scene of an assault left in such a pristine state. Besides the dry blood, there was no sign a struggle took place."

Gerlad mouthed something indecipherable. "Well, that just can't be possible."

"None of what has occurred recently seems possible either." She motioned to Gerlad. "Something is occurring in secret in this town. I know it is not safe for either of you, especially Elmyra. All of these instances have her name written on them, but I can't believe she could assault Mr. Akashi and then light the building on fire in her state. And you were with me."

When matters settled down later that evening, Ruthie set out from her home, making well sure to lock every door and window and to tell Gerlad not to leave the premises. She wore a veil to cover her face and moseyed throughout town, keeping to the subtlety of the shadows. Few people were out this late, and those that were either had no consciousness of their current state or were rather fond of the serenity of the cool night breeze and the secrecy of the dark.

A light pierced through the vaporous dusk. There was a gathering in one of the alleyways. A few familiar faces carried towards a faint light leading into an old cellar below one of the storefronts. Ruthie cautiously crept forward, hoping to listen in and get a glimpse of what was occurring within the ominous earthen crypt.

"We are wasting too much time with these games," a familiar voice said. Ruthie crept closer still, until the faint light caressed her face. It was Mrs. Iras, the florist. "We have waited so long for this culling; let's just do it."

The chief among the occult figures raised his hand in authority. It was Mr. Culden, the cobbler. He was known to most of the townsfolk as a reclusive figure, but here he was filled with a mysterious vigor. "No, the rest will have to willingly agree, or else this will not work. This town must be subject to his will."

"What else is to be done then?" another voice called out from the followers.

The room was filled with occult symbols and scarlet stained images of eyes. Candles set forth a faint light that appeared to struggle in its escape from the saturnine dungeon. "One last act. An encore. Mrs. Tilly's sacrifice was but an initiation, a willing invocation, though she realized not its severity. We must now guide him along the course."

"What about Ruthie?" There was a commotion and a bevy of whispers among the gathering folk.

Mr. Culden calmed them down in a single wave of his hand. "Ruthie is one of us; she has always done right by this town. Why, in fact, she has been helping us all this time; isn't that right, Ruthie?"

Ruthie saw the red eyes' deep gaze; they were joined with the rest of the gathering cult. She stood still. She was the center focus; she couldn't turn back now. She needed to fight and take back control of Parson's Fold, but there were so many of them, and she knew them all. Before she could realize it and react, she was surrounded. The macabre figures closed in; their eyes fixed upon her very soul. She had to do something—she had to escape.

Ruthie's veil rustled in the wind on the return journey home. Elmyra was bedridden and Gerlad was by her side, until he heard the bang on the front door and went to check. It was Ruthie. Gerlad let her in and was about to tell her of Elmyra's worsening condition, but something was wrong. The veil was familiar, yet the face behind the shroud was an uneven, unfamiliar sight. It came into view suddenly, that fiendish gaze; it wasn't Ruthie's—this thing wasn't Ruthie. Gerlad prepared an empyrean incantation to protect himself, but the light left his face. He fell down, crumbling in the darkness.

"Elmyra," the voice called. A writhing movement followed it down the hallway. "Elmyra, you have to come quickly, Gerlad needs your help. The town needs you."

"Ruthie, is that you?" Elmyra faintly said. She tried to bring herself to her feet, but she could barely stand. Her grip on reality was a mental lapse, a physical ailment sunk down to her spiritual core.

"Yes, it is me, Elmyra. I am here to help you," the voice said in an unsettling whisper. The figure caught Elmyra before she fell to the floor. "Let us see, Elmyra." She moved Elmyra's shirt to reveal a bruise near her neck. It was a red symbol, a pair of bloodied eyes. "Lovely, Elmyra, let us go to the townsfolk. They will be happy to see you, and I bet you will be happy to see them. Most importantly, our lord will be able to see once more. All he needs is just a bit of light."

Elmyra convulsed; she violently mumbled, struggling to break free from the sinister grip with whatever energy she could muster. The voice urged her forward; the figure forced her.

"Ruthie, why are you doing this?" Elmyra said with the last remnants of her fleeting energy.

The veil was removed. The face revealed was marred and damned, but it was familiar. Its eyes had cried once before; the tears they left had dried, leaving noticeable stains, visceral scars in the flesh. The zealous gaze of the damned Bethel Ager would not let her go; there was no turning back from this path.

Anointed in stolen incense, Elmyra was condemned as a murderous thief among the town. A ritualistic, surreptitious chant condemned her to an undeserved fate. "See here all of you, hark the cry of the criminal who has carried out these heinous acts. But avert thine eyes, for she deserves no mercy. Submit yourself to the call of Parson's Fold. To protect this town, this vile assailant must die. Elmyra Jansson, for the deaths of Mrs. Tilly Duvell, Ruthanne Nolta, Mr. Hiato Akashi, and even your own Gerlad Holfer you shall be hung and your face bagged—heard but never seen. You are set off into the dark," the executioner said aloud before the gathering crowd, which erupted in cheers.

Elmyra shed a few beloved tears, holding firm to her light, for it was all she had left. And then all went dark. A cry rang throughout Parson's Fold. It was an ancient, hellish scream. The unsuspecting townsfolk cowered and tried to flee as best as they could. Paldermen, the sightless, manipulative daemon, could now see, thanks to the sacrificial gift of light that the town of Parson's Fold had recklessly abandoned. They had crossed into the darkness; they were his.

Upon Laurel Roads

Within the great land of Graecoram, there lies a hilltop village named Verza, whose old narrow cobblestone roads lead out into the lush countryside where the finest laurel trees adorn the open world. Among the quaint stone villas on the outskirts of town, there once dwelled a humble man named Antonio Avalano, who was known by all the townsfolk as being kind, honest, and hardworking. He was a carpenter by trade, and he was one of the most seasoned carpenters in the small shop of Fallari & Sons Carpentry. His work was his passion, and though he earned a meager salary, he happily lived in his small house with his wife, Diana, and his three children, Joseph, Margaret, and Vincent.

He arose at the same time every morning to head to work. His boss, the owner of the business, was always satisfied with Antonio's craftsmanship, and he made his sentiments known each day. "Antonio, without you I don't know how we would survive!" his boss, Francesco Fallari, would say with great praise. And his words were part true: there were many carpentry stores within Verza, and it was extremely difficult to find good work for a reasonable price. Every bit of carpentry was done by hand, sometimes into the late hours of the night when only the light of candles would guide the hands of the carpenters, and Antonio always displayed his skill and expertise in such conditions.

When his work was done, Antonio would walk through the winding streets of Verza and the open laurel roads. Occasionally, Antonio would witness the sight of nobles, who would come from all over Asterra to pick the laurel leaves for their ceremonial brooches.

He could barely dream of what an honor it would be to be bestowed a brooch of laurel, but all would be forgotten when he reached his home and greeted his wife and children. Sometimes, he would present small gifts that he had built during his break at work for his children and wife. They would smile and cheer as they shared a pleasant meal, and Antonio would stay up a little longer and then go to bed early to start a new day in the same manner.

One morning, when Antonio had just begun his work, Francesco called him over. "Antonio you are my greatest worker, and you have been a friend to my father and to me for more years than I care to count. You deserve more money for your hard work," Francesco said with a warm, genuine look of gratitude upon his face. Antonio was flattered, but he knew well that Fallari & Sons had seen some difficulty trying to compete with the other stores, and if he agreed to take more money, that would mean less money for the business to operate. So being the kind man that he was, Antonio respectfully declined the offer.

"Are you sure, Antonio?" Francesco asked.

"Most positive. My work here is my life, and I am grateful for it every day," he proudly responded.

Francesco closed his eyes, smiled widely, and embraced Antonio like a brother. "You are a kind and great man, Antonio!"

That night, Antonio walked home along his usual path, gazing at the buildings in the town of Verza and then at the beautiful trees of laurel that graciously adorned the country roads and the limits of the town with their sweet leaves.

When Antonio arrived home, he greeted his wife and his children with a joyous embrace. His children smiled, and they received Antonio with such warmness that even the candles could hold no light to such adoration. The family gathered around the dinner table to eat, and Diana faintly smiled at her husband. "Antonio, were you able to earn enough money to go to the store today and buy some more bread? We have almost run out, and I don't have enough money in my savings to afford any more."

Antonio closed his eyes with a modicum of pain in his heart. He had very little money to buy bread, but it was just enough. "I have forgotten, Diana, but tomorrow I will buy some more bread. Tonight, we shall make do with what we have and be merry, for we have each other and our kind hearts!" Diana nodded her head in approval, and the family had dinner together, eating what little food they had left. When their meal was over, they said good night to each other and went off to bed.

The following day, Antonio had worked his entire shift creating a beautiful treasure chest, meant to hold the most valuable of possessions and which was almost ready to sell. His coworkers were amazed by his work, and they gave him great praise, which he returned with modest thanks and a genuine, yet taxing, smile. After work, Antonio headed towards the bakery to buy bread. He walked through the streets of Verza and, along his path, found a few coins that someone seemed to have left behind. He wondered for a moment if he should go ahead and pick them up, but he rebutted the concept, declaring it would be wrong to take someone else's money, for he was an honest man. He left the money on the street and went to the baker and bought the last loaf of bread there with the last of his wages, saying to himself that once he sold his crafted treasure chest he would make up for the money. So, Antonio happily went home, passing once again through the beautiful roads of laurel, feeling greatly honored by his decision.

He entered his home and greeted his wife and his children and presented the bread he had bought. His children were happy, and he was happy as well. After dinner, his wife went to him and reminded him that his oldest child, Joseph, was turning ten in a few days, and all that Joseph wished for was a new pair of shoes so that he would not hurt his feet when playing outside with his friends. Antonio thought to himself that he would need to have Francesco sell his treasure chest soon if he was to have enough money to buy his son a new pair of shoes. He was sad about squandering the opportunity to claim the spare coins on the road, but he reminded himself that he was an honest man, and he promised his wife that he would buy Joseph a splendid pair of shoes.

Antonio went to bed and woke up the following day and went to work. Much to his liking, Francesco was able to sell his beautiful

chest without him having to mention a word of his troubles. And as had been arranged, Antonio earned a small commission for the sale. After work, a few of his fellow workers wanted to go out to a local tavern in town for dinner and a few drinks to celebrate Antonio's big sale. Antonio agreed and decided to go out to eat. After the celebrations, his friends wanted to pay for his meal and drinks, but Antonio thought to himself that he was a hardworking man who took pride in his ability to pay for himself. So, Antonio refused the offer and decided, instead, to pay for his own meal and drinks with the commission he had earned. However, now, as he went home through town and made it upon the roads of laurel, he realized that he had not bought his son Joseph a pair of shoes, and he barely had enough money left to even do so.

The next day, Antonio told his wife that he had not yet been able to get a gift, and she was upset, for they had nothing to present Joseph for his birthday. Antonio had no idea what to do. It was now the weekend and the shop would close soon, and he had little money or time left to buy his son the gift he wanted. Antonio went to town and tried to find the coins he had seen on the street, but it seemed that someone else had taken the opportunity to seize them.

Antonio was distraught, and he couldn't help but feel miserable— the only thought that gave him a semblance of hope was his honor, which he still desperately held onto. He thought about it so much that he forgot what opportunities he had squandered and only thought of what good deeds he had performed. Surely, honor is noble, nobler than all the gilded coins in the world, but for Antonio, this embrace left him empty-handed.

He left the center of town and headed out to the countryside, following the country roads until his feet began to ache. He sat in the sun and tried to get away from the thought of disappointment he was envisioning in his mind. He gazed out towards the open world and watched the gentle breeze rustle the laurel leaves atop the well-kept trees and bushes. He felt at peace in the countryside, and his despair began to slowly leave, but a little while later, Antonio saw a man from afar that looked slightly disheveled in appearance. "Certainly, this man is worse off than I am," Antonio said as his sadness returned while watching the man wander alone through the fields.

He thought to approach the poor fellow, but the man, noticing Antonio's own despair, was, himself, moved with pity and approached Antonio. "What causes you such pain, good sir?" the traveler asked.

Antonio looked upon the face of the man, which was as rugged and worn as his clothes. "I have no money to buy my son a proper gift for his birthday. The world surely is cruel to a man who has given it such praise and honor. I have worked hard and asked for nothing extra in return; I have taken no coin that was not mine, and I have asked for no kind gesture that I did not deserve. My family lives on meager means. Surely, this is not an honorable world if I must struggle for doing what is right?" Antonio paused for a moment as he looked again at the man's disheveled attire. "You must know of this plight, though, my friend."

The man, hearing Antonio's words, reached into his pocket and procured a small pouch. "I unfortunately know not of what plight you speak of, good sir, but I have collected much coin, and I had intended to buy myself a gift with my money. But all your talk about honor surely makes me want to do a noble deed. So, take some of my coin, friend; you will benefit more from this money than I, for I have no family to take care of, and family, of course, is the most noble of all things in this life." The gesture moved Antonio to tears, and he hugged the man, and asked how he could repay him. The man declined and gave a warm farewell to Antonio. That night Antonio went home with a new pair of shoes for his son and promised to be a more reasonable man.

Michael Frank Rizzo

A Mid-Journey Rest

I t is always good to take a rest during any adventure, and I always like to check in, just to make sure I haven't put anyone to sleep with my storytelling. So, my friend, tell me, how are you enjoying your travels through Asterra so far? Do you have a favorite character or a favorite tale? Do you have a suggestion for your good friend, Penny, on where to travel to next?

Well, for now, I still have many other tales to tell! We still have about halfway to go before we reach our destination! The next few tales will bring you to pirate-infested shores, magical forests, mystical lakes, and many more wondrous locations. In fact, one of the tales in this next section is courtesy of an article written by my good friend Grimaldo Elwidget, which I think you will greatly enjoy. So what are we waiting for? Let's continue on with the journey!

Penny Rodgers

A Trial of Thieves

I t was a new spring day, and a simple, rejuvenating morning greeted
the foliage of Balri, the great market town and fiscal center of the
realm of Magris. It was a town of roughly ninety-thousand—
enough to blend in at one's personal leisure. And it was even easier for
Henry Stillton, who had only moved to Balri about six months prior
after a nomadic lifetime of traveling from town to town. He knew little
more than the colors of Magris' winter and budding spring, but he had
no intention to waste the moments of each precious day in indolent
wait. He had a new life to forge, and he knew this was the place.

The people were kind, always brimming with confidence and optimism, and they were always happy to see him. He had more friends
than he could count, and he felt like every day he made a few more.
"Good morning, Henry," his neighbor Simon said to him. "What a
wondrous surprise to see you this early," Thomas the candlemaker
said with a smile. Henry worked part-time in Ruth's floral shop, and
she proclaimed how Henry was the best help she had ever received.
And all Henry could think of was how fortunate he was to have finally
met such wonderful people.

At the start of every day, when the shop owners opened their
doors for business, Henry walked along the streets with a proud
smile. He felt he could gaze at the busy storefronts along the main
cobblestone thoroughfare for hours, dreaming of the possibilities
for success within Balri. The sounds of the stores' mechanical cash
registers filled the air with the music of commerce. Various coins
quickly changed hands, and on one particular day, a bit of commotion
arose over a few missing gild in one of the stores. Henry thought the

growing concern of a few townsfolk seemed a bit overzealous. In the end, the missing money was only a matter of a miscounting, but the speculation he could overhear from a few townsfolk reminded him of a past life, which stole a bit of his joy in that moment. But Henry assured himself that he was a changed man. He deserved to be happy, just like everyone else.

Every evening, when Henry returned home, he helped the elderly Mr. Thims with his chores. The old man seemed lonely, and his response to Henry's presence was always joyous and resound. He would stumble over and pat Henry on the shoulder with what remaining energy he could muster, for Mr. Thims could never miss the opportunity to greet the person who seemed to be his best friend.

This particular day was filled with many surprises, and on this evening, Mr. Thims was even livelier than usual. His legs didn't appear as stiff, and his eyes didn't seem as if they were lost in a gaze somewhere aforetime. "It is a great gift that you share, Henry. To notice people in all this commotion, no matter where they have been or where they are, is truly special. An old man might have continued to be forgotten if it wasn't for you, my dear friend."

Henry lightly chuckled. "How can I forget you; you always have so much stored on your property." Mr. Thims laughed and pointed his bony finger at Henry.

"When you get to be as old as I am, collecting becomes more of a lifestyle than a simple hobby. And the past seems just a bit more joyous every day." He paused for a brief moment. "But the future always seems far better when you share yours with me. And that is a happy thought." Henry, too, was happy to share these moments with Mr. Thims, and the future did seem bright for both of them, and afterwards, Henry returned home, carrying a bit of good on his shoulders.

Now, some would say this wasn't much, but this life was special for a simple man of average stature and modest age like Henry. And others might not understand, but it surely brought a faint smile to Henry's gentle face, which was slightly worn and tired. What he saw in the mirror every day was his, and he was happy, for he had his life ahead of him, and his past—well his past was far behind him. He had told himself many months ago that he was done being tired; that he was done being complacent. Along with his travels, his prior life consisted of an amalgamation of odd jobs, especially in the most recent years, and he had endured a certain hardship. But this year would be different.

Henry had been looking for a new job for a long time, and Ruth's floral shop, while nice, wouldn't sustain him for the rest of his days. Within the last few weeks, he had the opportunity to apply to a few promising careers. Each rejection was tough, but he yielded not to doubt, and within the next passing days, he received a letter from the owner of the leading masonry works in Balri; this one wasn't a rejection, and Henry was filled with joy.

"This is my moment," he said aloud to himself after reading the letter, "and I am not going to squander it." The letter informed him that he would have to interview with the owner, Deldun, tomorrow around noon. Henry was anxious about making a good first impression, and his friends in Balri gave many suggestions on what to wear and, most importantly, what to say. But Mr. Thims shook his head at the surfeit of suggestions. "Flashy clothes will just hide who you really are, Henry, and fancy words will just muddle what you wish to say. Just be who you were meant to be. I might not see all too well, but I see you, just as you see me, and that is a joy to behold."

Henry was happy for this advice. He knew well that he was capable of doing the job. He was good at working with his hands, and he was diligent and patient with every job he approached. And so he grew confident that he would make a good first impression.

The morning came and he was ready, and his friends in Balri couldn't have been more excited for him. "Best of luck, Henry. Any job would be honored to have you," his neighbor Simon said. "You are a good man, and good things will always come to you," Thomas the candlemaker said. "Best of luck to the person who always puts a smile on my face," Ruth the florist said. This was his opportunity, and he was ready.

He walked into Deldun's Masonry with poise and optimism. It was as pleasant a feeling as he had imagined. "It is a pleasure to meet you, Henry," Deldun happily said as he welcomed Henry into his office.

Henry graciously smiled. He had a good feeling, one that he hadn't felt in a while, and the old-world shop, filled with piles of various stones, felt like a sanctuary to him. "It is a pleasure to meet you as well, Deldun." They both sat down and the conversation continued for what seemed like hours. It was effortless for Henry.

Deldun was impressed, and he folded his hands and laid them on his desk as he leaned forward and intently looked at Henry. "I think this interview went very well. I believe you will be great for the job, and I know we will be happy to have you here. There is just one last thing we will need to do to finish up."

Henry sat attentively as he waited for Deldun to continue. "We will just need to ask around, and check a few of the places you previously lived and worked. This is just to make sure that everything is good with you, which I am sure it is. We'll send out a carrier bird, first thing tomorrow, to contact the appropriate parties. It won't take too long, Henry, and soon enough you'll be one of us."

Henry meticulously ran his hand through his hair as he blankly stared at the wall in front of him and noticed an idyllic painting hanging there. He inhaled deeply as he cracked a nervous smile, hoping to draw attention away from his momentary pause. "Of course, shouldn't be a problem. That is a nice picture." He casually pointed, and Deldun turned his head quickly and gave a light nod.

"Yes, it depicts the bloom of the blue rose of Magris—new life in all its wonder and beauty. Spring here is like no other place in the world," Deldun said. Henry couldn't agree more, and he rose and shook Deldun's hand, and the two parted ways for the day.

Everything went well, Henry thought, but an intrusive doubt followed him on the way home. His friends asked him how the interview went, and he gave an optimistic answer, serving more to reassure himself than anything else. However, there was one problem, which he no longer felt he could escape.

Henry was once a prolific thief, and though he had changed for the better, such trials of his past seemed to haunt him no matter how far he traveled. But he was hoping this time would be different; he was hoping to keep this new life of his.

Several days passed, and Henry didn't hear a word. He waited patiently for the mail on his porch, but each morning he was disappointed when he didn't find the letter he was hoping for.

Yet word had traveled—but it was one he didn't know of, and one he surely wasn't hoping for. After some extensive searching, Deldun's team had found out about Henry's past and had told Deldun all about it. Seeing as thievery was the case, Deldun wasn't comfortable having Henry work for him, but more importantly, he wasn't comfortable with the idea of having Henry living in a vibrant, peaceful town such as Balri.

So Deldun decided to bring this newly found information about Henry Stillton to the mayor, who then decided to bring it to the town council. They were shocked; many of the council members knew Henry personally, and they felt betrayed by his dishonesty. In the following days, they decided to hold a secret meeting to discuss the prospect of what to do with Henry Stillton; meanwhile, Henry waited patiently within the comforts of his own house, still desperately holding onto optimism as he checked each day for a letter in his mailbox.

In Balri, talk spread further among the townsfolk, and the monthly town hall meeting was stacked to the brim with denizens from all over town. They had come to voice their complaints about Henry Stillton, and they didn't wish to hold back a single thought.

"He is an odd and strange man, and we surely aren't honored to see him roam around this town. He never has anything nice to say," Henry's neighbor Simon said.

"He is a wicked man, with wicked intentions," Thomas the candlemaker added, as the council chamber roared with approval.

"His very presence always puts a frown on my face, and he scares my customers away," Ruth the florist said. The crowd grew louder with every complaint.

The head councilor lightly caressed his beard as he pondered the situation. "This is not an easy task, but I am in agreement with the people about what must be done," he said to his peers.

The lawmakers agreed, and the decision to remove Henry from Balri was about to be rendered effective when a small old man walked into the council hall. He had a cane, which was more for guiding his tired eyes than for supporting his body. "My name is Mr. Thims, and I have noticed Mr. Henry, and he was the only one who noticed me. My eyes do not see well, and my legs do not move fast, but he was my eyes and my support when I needed it most, and with him I saw just as much as anyone else could, but they still didn't see me. And even now I feel as if my poor sight is not such a rarity among this congregation. But yours is a different blindness, one that abandons values which cannot be seen."

The local cleric scoffed at the notion. "This thief has run from town to town—probably in hopes to recommit his past crimes. However, he was exposed, and these towns, rightfully, didn't hold back their hand of justice; why should our decree be any different? Why should we give him a chance when no one else has? He is a thief—nothing more, nothing less."

The old man put his head down in dismay; there was nothing else he could do, and he knew it well; the council's mind was resolute on their decree, and the townsfolk were in adamant agreement: Henry Stillton did not belong within the town of Balri anymore.

Following the meeting, Henry received a letter, but it was not the one he had hoped for. He opened it vigorously, but his head lowered, his heart puttered, and his breath was still as he approached the final few remarks of the letter. He was to leave Balri by the end of the week, or he would be personally escorted out. He had nowhere to go, and his friends were no more.

He quickly packed his things and thought to leave in the shroud of night in hopes of not seeing anyone; or rather, so that no one would see him. He thought to stop by and say farewell to Mr. Thims, but he figured that the old man wouldn't wish to see him—though this was the furthest from the truth. So Henry finished packing and then he left quickly, while quietly saying goodbye to the town he used to love.

The night was dark, and he could barely see in front of him. As he was departing Balri and leaving the outskirts of town, a horse and

carriage came upon him fast. The driver didn't see Henry and hit him as he was crossing the road.

Henry died immediately, clutching a small blue rose in his hand that he had taken as a memento of Balri. Word spread around town, and most of the citizens didn't care at all about poor Henry, continuing on with their day without remorse. They were glad that there were no more thieves living within Balri.

They continued to gather and see each other just as they normally had. Yet old Mr. Thims had now become fully blind, and he couldn't see. His legs became weaker, and he couldn't walk. And there was no Henry to help him. At night, a cool winter wind blew, and the blue roses of Balri all withered and died, and the blossom of life was stolen away.

An Aquamarine Heart

There is a place in the realm of Saires where a series of trails carry on throughout a misty majesty of wandering woods that eventually yield to the natural beauty of the famed Mirist Lake. Within the center of those murky waters, there lies a small island, which was once home to a great serpentine beast who guarded a magnificent treasure replete with precious diamonds, gems, and gold. Proud and stalwart, he was the perfect custodian for this hoard of riches of ancient kings and queens. And as tasked, the great serpent swam throughout the lake, never once departing from its lacustrine shoals.

Left to the majesty of its own mist, Mirist Lake became a site of legend—a place that the folks of the neighboring villages were far too afraid to ever set foot near. Word spread, by horse and bird, daylight and lamplight, of what treasure could possibly be secured within the small island of the lake. Tales of the hoard of riches contributed to the fortune's growing grandiosity for everyone but its guardian, and in time the great serpent grew bored and old in age.

The serpent could remember when he had roamed freely, but the memory was too distant to bring about any semblance of joy. At an early age, he had been taught by a wise sage that those who had amassed the treasure of the lake had believed it to be the key to eternal happiness. And that being chosen to guard such treasure was an honor, and such duty made him the keeper and giver of happiness. Alas, safeguarding the treasure was a lonely, taxing business. Petty robbers, seeking to take advantage of his weary state, were his only company, and he began to question what people chose to keep close to their hearts.

To appease his doubts, he called out to a few sairien owls, whose intellectual conversations he had listened to from his small island. He spoke to them sweetly and asked them to send word out to the neighboring towns and kingdoms that whoever was to bring him a true treasure greater than what he guarded would be rewarded with the most precious item from the fortune. Word soon spread throughout all of the lands, and great nobles, worthy adventurers, and valiant knights came to the shoals of the majestic Mirist Lake to show the great serpent their wondrous treasures and heirlooms. There were crowds of visitors, and it was the most people the great serpent had ever seen in his life. For what seemed liked the first time, the serpent witnessed a glimpse of life outside of Mirist Lake. He was excited, for all of these travelers surely had tales to tell of the world outside, and their treasures could surely stand testament to such grandeur.

Happily, the serpent went from heirloom to artifact and from ornament to relic, but his countenance changed ever so slightly with each item. Alas, these treasures were very much the same as what he guarded within the small island in the center of the lake, and they lacked the spark that he very much desired to see. And the visitors fought among themselves, each claiming their treasure to be more important than the other, and this caused the serpent much more added sadness, for it did little to change his doubts.

The great serpent, after much sorrow, towered before the great crowd of people surrounding the lake. His sagacious old face was filled with disappointment, and the people were apprehensive to react. The serpent said for all the travelers to hear, "Is treasure the same to all people? Is its only purpose to cause such feelings of glittering contempt? Its value determined only in what it reflects and not what it instills? Surely, there is more purpose to these fortunes?" Yet there was not one answer put forth to change his mind, and each one of the travelers soon left, and the serpent stood all by himself, guarding the treasure as he was used to doing.

One cold day, a young girl found her way to the lake after overhearing a few local townsfolk talking about the great treasure hidden on the small island and the challenge presented by the guardian serpent. As she approached the lacustrine shoals of the lake, the great serpent surfaced to greet her. He stood nigh ten meters tall, and his long body, brightly glistening with an azure reflection, stretched far below the water's surface. This was a sight to scare most, but not the young girl, who had traveled far with only—what most would deem—a meager assortment of items.

"Little girl, who are you, and what brings you to my lake?" the great serpent said.

"My name is Medriel, and I heard of your challenge. I am here to present you a treasure of mine."

The serpent looked confused at the very thought. "What treasure could a little girl like you possess? I have met with knights and mages, princes and princesses, kings and queens, and they all failed to present me a treasure that might bring a light to my weary state. What is it that you bring that might be so important?"

The little girl knew little of these other adventurers' items, only of what she carried with her, and that meant enough for her. So, she took out the small item and presented it before the great serpent.

The serpent could barely see it at first, and only after moving his head closer could he make out the shape and workings of a battered pendant that seemed to show the scars of a great conflict. "I found this pendant in the broken and war-torn city of Prescus—my first home," she said with a modicum of pain, as if reliving the experience. "I was lost to everyone, and that is what I, too, came to believe. But the owner of this pendant, and those who stood in that city defending it, never gave up on me. I don't know their names, not even that of the original owner of this pendant, but they aren't lost. Every day, I find my way on the road just a bit better than yesterday, and now it feels like I am never lost at all. I think every road brings me a bit closer to the souls who never abandoned me."

The great serpent looked down at the girl, and his apathetic countenance slowly faded as a melancholic, glossy hue subdued his eyes, offset by a small, earnest smile that cut through the dense air. "Now, through the mist I see what true treasures lie in this world, and surely this is among its greatest. Sadly, meaning is often lost in time, for materialism is not simply an obsession with objects but more so a misinterpretation of their meaning and purpose. But this was never lost on you, and that is a reason to smile, for oh, what joy your tale brings to me."

The serpent rested his body upon the shoals of the lake. "Little girl, I have grown weary with old age, and my life has been confined to this lake, guarding treasure that is not even mine in hopes that it brings happiness. But when my time is over, I would like for you to have a great heirloom of mine, so that maybe you can also carry it wherever you go."

The little girl happily nodded her head and returned with a smile of her own. "I would be more than happy to."

Every day from that moment on, the girl came to visit the great serpent and share with him tales of the world from her journeys; he reveled in thought and dreamed hundreds of dreams till the day came when he finally closed his eyes and slept forever, and the little girl wept ever so greatly.

The fortunes the serpent guarded passed to new stewardship, and the rest of the folks were upset that no one could claim the grand treasure. However, left behind on the misty shoals of the lake, overlooked by all, was the large aquamarine heart of the serpent, glowing brightly as it pierced through the darkness. It was the little girl's to receive, and she did so graciously; and as promised, when she became a woman and a great adventurer, she carried the serpent's aquamarine heart with her wherever she went. And that great serpent, once confined to the lacustrine shoals of Mirist Lake, saw the whole world, and what a treasure that truly was.

THE SECRET OF NORMAN'S POINT

R odolfo could think of nothing but the pungent smell of warm
sulfur mixed with the saltiness of the fresh ocean air while
looking at the wild sight of Salerina. His stomach was sick
from the presence of unpredictable commotion, and he knew her
usual tricks were far from over. Yet he was hesitant to let her go. *Not
yet,* he kept reminding himself, as she got her sorts together in the
small hideout. He needed her expertise, and he would just have to
endure the brashness and recklessness that stuck to her worse than
the intoxicating smell of dying gunpowder that filled the room.

His nostrils flared, inhaling and releasing the lingering smoke
from the few candles that adorned their presence with faint light,
revealing the singular color displayed on his fair countenance—a
reddish rage. "Trouble will follow you far past the grave, which, given
your latest stunt, might not be too far away."

Salerina threw her leather jacket aside, relieving herself of the
poignant sulfur aura that followed her. She then proceeded to run
her hand through her damp, messy curls, removing the sand hidden
within her sea of light-brown hair. "I was expecting a warm thank
you, Roldy, and maybe a jolly welcome. Of course, that is what friends
would normally say."

Rodolfo rolled his eyes. "Well, thanks to you, we may never get
our hands on whatever lies within Norman's Point."

Salerina popped open her flask, took a swig of whatever concoc-
tion was brewing inside, and took a seat. "'Our'? 'We'?" She smirked.
"Does this mean we're finally teaming up after all? What makes you
think I would even say yes to such an offer?" She crossed her legs and

set her right arm perpendicular to the table, letting her brown eyes dazzle with amusement in the dancing flames.

He had to think about it again for a moment himself. Was he crazy? Surely so, but not as crazy as her, and he needed as much craziness as he could dare find in this remote stretch of land overlooking the vastness of the Sillian Ocean. He sat down at the table to join Salerina in a standoff gaze. "You'll do it because I know you want whatever treasure lies in Norman's Point more than I do."

"And . . ." she quickly added.

"And you might just know a thing or two about how to sneak past those scoundrels that are in our way."

Salerina smirked. It wasn't every day a prolific pickpocket, locksmith, and rogue swashbuckler was complimented by a renowned adventurer.

"Normally, I would say no, but we have been on many adventures together, Roldy, so for you, I'll give it a shot."

"Hopefully not the same one that blew up that ship," he said.

She quickly stood to her feet and flamboyantly put her hands to her side. "I bet we'll find that out tonight," she said, leaning forward slightly over the table.

Rodolfo shook his head and soon stood up to join her. "So, what is our plan?"

"I figure we walk around for a bit; maybe something good will come to me after taking in the sights and fresh air."

"Are you serious?" Rodolfo said, stopping in his tracks.

She nonchalantly waved her hand in the air. "Don't worry. I've explored every providence of Del' San Cove."

"Including Norman's Point?"

"No, but I bet it's quite similar to all of the rest."

"I beg to differ. I've been around this coastline many times, and there are still many secrets hidden within these coves and shoals."

Salerina nodded her head calmly. "You're right; you are the far more experienced adventurer, and your skill as an iconographer has discovered many great treasures. But how well do you think that will hold up in a fight?"

Rodolfo laughed. "Time apart from stalking me surely didn't kill your charm. In fact, you and your mischievous ways beat me here. So your craft has only improved, or perhaps you found another way here?" He paused briefly. "Maybe we each say how we found out about the growing interest in Norman's Point? Should help with getting our plans in order."

There was immediate silence. Salerina suggestively looked at him. "Not how I do business. You start first, dear," she said with a smile.

He knew she wouldn't budge, and they didn't have time to waste. "A certain tale seemed to travel quickly to the village of Rezsev where I was lodged in southern Eurus. Something about phantom ships sounding strange signals off the Sarcino Coast. It has scared many ships and folks away except the thieves and pirates, so if it was worth it to them, I decided to put some stock in investigating the true cause of the commotion."

"And have you found the reason for the motley, malevolent crowd that joins us on our hunt?"

"You don't know?" He scoffed lightly. "Does the name Algreven Lockjaw sound familiar to a fellow . . ." He paused, awkwardly locking his gaze on Salerina.

"A fellow what?" she said.

"A fellow sea-loving adventurer," he said calmly yet quickly.

She licked her top teeth with restraint hidden behind a cool countenance. "I know a bit, but go ahead."

"Evidently, most of these pirates believe that the old pirate lord Algreven has returned from the depths of the sea to smite those who betrayed him in the mutiny many years ago and to reward those who stood by his side. Many are here to pledge loyalty—mostly out of fear, of course. Algreven knows how to rally his kind, huh?" he said with a nod.

"And the others?"

"From what it seems, the brigands are here just for the loot, and the rest of the pirates and scoundrels are a part of the same crew that betrayed him; the latter believe this to be a last-ditch curse of Algreven's to scare those away from his lost treasure, and the former are too destitute to care for their fate. Either way, we best hurry before the templar decide to intervene."

"How much of this tale do you actually believe?" Salerina asked.

"I am not too keen in believing stories that nature does not support: no law of magic or science can describe half of what I have heard, but behind every folktale there is a bit of truth. They say whoever led the mutiny against old Algreven stole an important treasure from him and hid it in secret for their use only. However, after sealing the treasure away, the keepers were killed and the treasure was lost in Norman's Point. This treasure just might be the one truth behind this whole tale."

She nodded her head delightfully. "Good, that is the only part I care about. Now, I can tell you a bit of what I have found about these pirates in my time here. I believe it might help us, because let's face it, Roldy, it has been quite some time since your last great, daring adventure."

He stopped in his tracks. "So, you are already hiding something?"

"Well, those pirates didn't just chase us for no reason."

"Chase you," he interjected.

"Okay, yes, well, I might have found a little secret." She reached into a satchel that dangled from her side and slowly pulled out her hand to reveal a small stone containing a few etchings. Rodolfo's eyes dazzled with excitement. Salerina said, "I stole it from a few of those lesser thieves who were guarding it, but I must say I have no idea what the excitement is about."

Rodolfo scoffed. "Don't even know what you're stealing, ey?"

She gave a facetious, innocent shrug. "Value is a man-made creation, darling, I just follow along with the crowd."

He grabbed the semilarge stone from her, held it near his lantern, and looked at the engravings. He happily took in the discovery for a moment. Salerina alternated between a few trifles in her gear and equipment, looking around while shooing the time away. "So, what did I get? Worth anything?"

"How you use it will determine its value."

She gave him a confused look. "And what does that mean for us, Roldy?"

He smiled. "It means that if we follow the icons on this stone, it will lead us to the sister stone, which will then lead us directly to the treasure."

"And you got all of that from a bit of etchings on a rock?"

He chuckled a bit, bringing the rock towards her and holding it to the light. "You didn't look at this very much, I take it?"

She saw the etchings; besides a few unfamiliar words and patterns, the images were quite straightforward. "Well, even if I did, how would I know where to go next?"

He conceded. "True, well, I guess it will be like old times a bit; you'll just have to follow me."

"I like to think that will be changing rather quickly once the pirates enter the picture," she said with a jovial smile.

The duo headed up to a nearby stone spire, which was covered in shoal-like shrubbery, to look out over the great vastness of the Sillian Ocean and the Sarcino Coast that greeted it. The lights from Port Town, Elgith, and Cedar Side Cottages dazzled from afar in the shroud of twilight. "Here," Rodolfo said. "Here is where I believe we'll have to go to place the stone and retrieve the second one."

"The Sunken Gardens?" She sighed, looking at Rodolfo's finger on the map. "It'll take forever to scavenge through that mess of briny pools and crowded reefs."

"No, it won't, because right here it shows that all we have to do is locate the coral tunnel that leads into the smallest pool. Underneath that tunnel is a slot that this stone fits into. And if I am interpreting these images correctly, the second stone should contain the map to the treasure. I surmise the main challenge will be behind us from there on."

Right after he uttered the last word, Salerina tackled him to the ground. His head cracked against the grainy earth. His lantern shattered near him. He desperately wondered if his usefulness in this unprecedented union had expired. A loud *bang* cut through the swirling maritime air. No, he was not betrayed—he was lucky. The stubborn, rough-cut foliage could no longer hide the eager assassin who crouched behind it.

Rodolfo could faintly see Salerina roll off him and reach to her side to draw her own firearm. *Bang*—a second shot cracked in the night. This one did not miss. The assassin fell dead, but he was not alone; another revealed himself and shot at Salerina, clipping her leather armor. She jolted slightly, but her hand was steady; she fired again, hitting the second assailant in his lower side. He dropped his gun and staggered forward. Unarmed, he attempted to charge towards her. She quickly evaded him and drew her sword. Making a quick, clean strike, she felled the second assailant quickly upon the rocky earth.

Salerina looked around cautiously. The surrounding vegetation held no more secrets this night. She inspected the firearms, tossing one aside and taking the other for later use. Rodolfo was still a bit dazed. She brushed the sand off him and gently helped him sit up. "Here is a trick of the trade: don't ever mention how little left there is to do, especially when there are this many scoundrels about looking for the same treasure," she said.

He rubbed his forehead. "I'll make sure not to forget." He opened his eyes and looked around, seeing the two dead assassins nearby. He looked at Salerina. "Thank you for that."

She waved her hand effortlessly in the air. "You can thank me by leading us to the treasure."

"Yes, of course." He carefully stood up. "I'll lead the way. Shouldn't be much farther." She gave him a curious look. "Oh, yes, I must get used to that."

They moved closer towards the coastline with every step as they descended from the rocky spire. The sounds of distant waves sloshing against the shore filled the salty air. Salerina fixed her eyes on the Sillian Ocean and indulged in a light sigh. "Ah, there is no place like the ocean. To be on a ship, riding the tides—there is no greater adventure." They continued walking until they could see where the Sunken Gardens' crowded estuaries cut through the Sarcino Coast.

Joined in the swirling night sky's dazzling stars, the estuaries many lifeforms colored the corals in luminescent wonder. They lit the way through the shallows in which the duo carefully trudged. The pair sloshed through the briny water until Rodolfo came to a stop. "I think we might have found the spot," Rodolfo said, as he pointed over at a small pool alit with colorful algae. "See the tunnel in the shallows?"

Salerina's eyes gave their own dazzle. "Yes, alright, let's get this over with. I don't like loitering in any place for too long."

Rodolfo led the way, and when they arrived, he patiently felt around the underside of the small tunnel for the rock-like indentation. "Ah, yes, I have it," he said. He put their engraved stone in carefully. There was silence for a moment as they both looked onward anxiously. Suddenly, a sound emanated from the tunnel; it started out low but then grew exponentially louder. The tunnel cut into two halves and retreated into the pool's walls. A coral spire emerged from the floor, dazzled in a unique golden glow. Atop sat a small glass orb, which the trail of light made its way up to, slowly but steadily. When the light finally reached the top, the orb sent out a magnificent beam into the night sky that seemed to carry onward for miles.

They looked on in amazement, until a second light cut through the sky from the other side of Norman's Point. Rodolfo was shocked; he wished he could read their engraved stone again. Salerina slowly turned her head towards him. He thought of what to say, but he wasn't so sure himself. "I must have interpreted the stone wrong. The second stone isn't for us to find here; it has already been found. They both are leading to the treasure." He frantically motioned onward. "Quickly, we must be on the move; whoever activated the second beacon must already be on the way to the treasure."

"Do you know where you're going?" Salerina said.

"Yes, I know a shortcut that should get us there much quicker than whoever races us." They cut through the Sunken Gardens and then whizzed through the pointed shrubbery and prickled vegetation that dotted the inland beyond the sandy shores. Rodolfo was moving quicker than he had ever moved in his life. He knew his error, and he wasn't about to make another one. They followed the beam of light to the base of a large hill. Rodolfo looked up; the light pointed towards the top. "Let's go," he said, "almost there."

Once at the top, they could hear the distant sounds below of another group. Salerina went to the other side of the hill. "We don't have much longer, so hurry up and find this treasure so we can get out of here. I am not looking forward to saving you a second time, Roldy."

He frantically looked around, but there seemed to be nothing to look for. He tried to think, but he was too unnerved to put his thoughts together. He put his head down and massaged his forehead with his hands, and he stood that way until Salerina called out. "Roldy, pay attention. We got some trouble." She pulled out her pistol and then took out the other one and a pouch of ammo and threw both to Rodolfo. "You know how to use it?"

He nodded his head. "Good, get ready." Soon, from among the brush and vegetation on the other side of the hill, a group of pirates emerged. There had to be at least ten of them. The leader did not shy away. He stood out among his rugged crew in his pristine gray leather coat and meticulously fitted captain's hat.

"Look here." He motioned to his lot. "We got a few fellow treasure hunters. Better than the rest, too." A few of them chuckled. "You must be quite the team to brave this land on such a night."

Salerina stood firm. "You talk a lot, but it appears your crew are the ones that do all the fighting. Heck, I shan't be surprised if they carried you up here," she said.

He brushed it off, but just barely. "You best be careful with your words; you're outgunned. So why don't you put down your weapons and help us find the treasure. We'll ensure that you get your fair share."

Rodolfo put his gun down to his side. He hesitated. "I guess that's a fair proposition," he said.

Salerina cautiously turned her head and shot Rodolfo an angry and confused look. "Are you crazy?"

He slowly nodded. "Must be the crack to the head; I must be a bit unstable." He subtly motioned her to step back towards him and look down. "We'll put our weapons down slowly," he announced. Salerina was still a bit unsure of Rodolfo's plan, until she stepped near him and saw a small stone like the one they had used earlier. It appeared to be hot, as a faint steam was rising out from a multitude of surrounding cracks that were spreading through the rocky earth beneath their feet. The ground seemed ready to give way from even the slightest disturbance. "Ready?" he said to her. She nodded slowly. He quickly discharged his pistol into the ground and stamped on the stone; the rocky earth below them collapsed, and they fell through the hole that had opened into the hollow hill.

The drop was over twenty meters into a fresh pool of blue, iridescent water. They both gasped for air when they surfaced. "Now we're even," Rodolfo said after he caught his breath.

"You really are nuts," Salerina said with a laugh. They could still hear the commotion above from the yells of the pirate captain. "We best think of our next move. Any other crazy suggestions?" Salerina said.

Rodolfo looked around and saw the opening of a small underwater tunnel near the floor of the grotto. "Are you a good swimmer?"

"Yes, quite good in fact. I wouldn't have blown up that ship before if I wasn't," she said with a smile.

He shook his head. That was all he needed to hear. Natural light from the aquatic vegetation and fauna lit their path as they dove under the water and quickly swam for the tunnel. Once inside, they heard a few splashes above. The pirate captain seemed to have finally convinced his men to make the plunge. Rodolfo could see the end of the tunnel in sight and the sweet sanctity of the surface above. Bursting through the aquatic plane, they let out a relieving exhale and graciously gasped for air. They had no idea where they were, but it was a large hidden cove, too large to be under the same hill they had climbed before; this cavern must have been built subtly under the undulating rocky landscape that connected the hill and forest to the coastline.

Rodolfo looked for a possible way out; Salerina looked for the treasure. Both of them had no idea where to start. They swam to a small coast across the cavern surrounded by the luminant features of lumbra moss and aljamer-röner. It lit their way to a small clear patch of sand. There, Salerina spotted a faint reflection. "Look." She motioned. "I think we found the treasure."

To their disappointment, though, they approached only to find what appeared to be a swashbuckler's sword. Rodolfo could see small writing on its hilt that read *Tide Shifter*. "There must be more," Salerina said, desperately looking around.

Rodolfo was also a bit confused. He was apprehensive at first to grab the sword, but his disappointment piqued his curiosity. Pulling it out of the sand, he turned around, only to be greeted by the sight of the pirate crew and their leader. Their weapons were drawn, and this time they were eager to use them.

"Give me the sword," the captain said. He extended his hand. "The likes of you don't deserve the privilege of wielding it. It is my right to lead the pirates of Del' San Cove. Pirate Lord Stivens sounds good, doesn't it, lads?" he said, rallying his crew.

Salerina shrugged. "This time I do intend to fire my weapon. Feel free to pick anyone besides Stivens—he's my target," she said to Rodolfo.

Rodolfo checked his pistol; he hadn't loaded another round, and it seemed he had lost the pouch of ammo that Salerina had given him during the fall. All he had to rely on was the sword; he held it close to his side, moving it ever so slightly as they slowly neared the water on order from Stivens by gunpoint.

"They say the blade is a treasure magnet," one of the crew members delightedly said.

"That and much more, they say. And it is ours," Stivens said, before refocusing his attention on Salerina and Rodolfo. "Now, lay it down on the sand, then turn around and walk ten paces to your grave."

Rodolfo grasped the blade with both hands before he went to place it on the ground. But a serendipitous discovery stilled his body; the water in the cave behind the crew slushed slightly with a sudden movement. "What was that?" one of the crew members said.

"Stay focused," Stivens barked.

Only Rodolfo had noticed that the name on the sword's hilt was not unwarranted: it had the ability to move water and change the tides. And Stivens's crew were conveniently not too far from the water, standing on the sandy salient of the shore. Rodolfo thought his movement out carefully. He went to place the sword down, bending over, but then made a swift slicing motion with its blade.

Salerina watched as a wave of water followed the dull side of the sword, the front blade cutting along the surface of the water, swirling it in a chaotic frenzy of tumultuous foam that shook loose the cavernous ceiling's many stalactites. Stivens and his crew were swept off their feet, a few falling into the cavern's frothing water. The remaining crew discharged their weapons in vain as another quick swing of the sword brought another wave of water down upon them. Stivens was swept into the water; he took aim with his pistol in a desperate attempt to end the mighty surge of water, but Rodolfo struck down with the blade, almost parting the great pool of water, tossing Stivens and his crew all about the cavern, until the pirates and their captain were consumed by the raging tides.

The water was so great in force that it knocked back a weakened makeshift stone wall that was hidden along the cavern's natural enclosing. Light poured into the cavern as the waves subsided. Rodolfo and Salerina could see the Sillian Ocean where it glowed in the rays of the rising morning sun. Reentering the water, they left the cavern behind, and from the small salient of ocean that was now adjoined to the water of the cave, they swam towards the flanking shores of the Sarcino Coast. Soon they could feel the sand beneath their feet and hear the calm tide of ocean on the shore.

"The breeze is a sailor's delight," Salerina said. She looked towards the ocean. "I wish I could be out there on a ship of my own. Was a first mate once; closest I got." She smiled.

He paused, keeping his gaze on the calm tides. Afar, two ships were silhouetted on the horizon. "And what happened?"

"A mild disagreement; quite common in my line of work."

He laughed. "I bet it is."

"But I'll be a captain yet, just you wait, Roldy. Think about it; there are islands and lands out there that neither of us have yet seen. And I might even be able to provide you with some transportation free of charge, if the loot is good," she said with an amicable smile.

"I'm a treasure magnet, don't you worry," he said. His eyes stayed fixated on the distant ocean. Along the horizon, a few more ships appeared, and then a few others after that, until there were over two dozen ships closing in on the very spot of shore on which they stood.

"Not fishing and transport ships, I suppose?"

Salerina could faintly make out the sails as the ships cut through the water. They weren't any pirate sails she had seen in recent years. And they carried an old symbol that hadn't been used in some time. "Algreven," she said coldly.

"What?" Rodolfo staggered. "He was swept away to sea . . . wasn't he?"

"Pirates like him are hard to kill. The dead don't want him among their ranks, it appears. Come on now, we got to get off the shore."

Rodolfo turned to follow Salerina, but they were met with the sight of at least a dozen pirates. They looked far different from Stivens and his crew.

One of them stepped forward. "I think Algreven would be offended if you were to leave without saying hello." He smiled and showed his grimy teeth and then spat on the sand near his feet. "Turn around and walk to the water." He pointed with his pistol drawn. When they arrived at the foamy edge of the ocean, they were stripped of their weapons.

The ships stopped in the distance. Salerina and Rodolfo could see two small rowboats embarking from what appeared to be the flagship among the fleet. The ferrymen approached slowly through the waves, until the two boats stood in the shallows waiting for their new passengers. "Move it," the pirate said, jabbing his pistol into Salerina's back. Rodolfo shot him a vicious gaze as they moved into the shoals towards the rowboats.

The water sloshed around as the duo and the rest of Algreven's pirate crew from shore entered the rowboats one by one. "Algreven's sure going to be happy to see that sword of his. You two might just live long enough to see him use it." The pistol-bearing pirate laughed, along with the rest of the crew on the crowded rowboats. Several of them were missing teeth, and they all smelled of something awful, but this was a minor inconvenience compared to what awaited ahead.

Soon the rowboats stopped alongside Algreven's ship. The name *Marengeld* was seen just above the second row of cannons on the starboard side. On the deck, the whole crew was awaiting their arrival. After chaining Salerina and Rodolfo tightly by the wrists and ankles, the crew gathered closer in anticipation, like sharks feeding on the hopes of a grand spectacle at the expense of the less fortunate.

And there he was. He cut through the crowd in a slow approach. He wore a great brownish-gray coat, which covered him almost down to his calves. His boots were black, matching the color of his short beard. He didn't take his eyes off them for a second. And Rodolfo couldn't help but stare back at the large cut upon Algreven's right cheek, which ran along his jawline.

He walked towards them, easing the tension with a subtle smile. "I see you have found my sword. It is just as I remembered it." His eyes gleamed in the sword's generous shimmer. "Just as it was when it was used to set me off to sea thirty years ago," he added. The right side of his mouth could barely move.

"You should have drowned out there. You gave us lot a bad name," Salerina said.

He leisurely inched closer to them. "Yes, I felt like it at times. The ocean is such a lonely place. Thankfully, I found a few new friends out there, who were kind enough to bring me to the Fire Islands. Nothing like a vacation when a target is painted on yer head." He looked around. "And what a welcome home. Faces have changed during the years, but they're still dirty as ever." A tumultuous roar of laughter erupted from both the old and new pirates of Algreven's crew. "It is good to be back," he continued. "Now with my sword rightfully by my side, nothing will stop us from taking over Del' San Cove. Just the sight of a few loyal ships along the midnight tide has turned many rightfully away. And the horns of Algreven have called more of the loyal forward. Now Del' San Cove will harken back to the glory pirate days of old."

Algreven grabbed his sword from his first mate. "Just as sharp as ever," he said, with gleaming pride.

But just as he said this, a large fleet of ships became visible in the distance. These were not pirate ships from the look of them as they quickly approached, growing larger on the horizon. No, the sun shined upon their sails and revealed the sacrosanct symbol of the Templar Order, and they had no intention of surrendering northern

Del' San Cove to pirates, especially not to the likes of Algreven's crew.

Terms were surely to be set between Algreven and the templar—well, this was what Rodolfo believed. But Salerina was far wiser in the affairs of pirates. The cannons were fired from the *Marengeld* without delay; the rest of the pirate ships followed suit. The templar ships took evasive maneuvers; they, too, were familiar with the affairs of pirates. Leading their fleet was no other than Grand Admiral Diana Harper, who had made quite the name for herself on the northern coasts of Asterra. Her ship, the *Adjudicator*, pressed ahead with the rest of the fleet.

The templar ships were quick; their sails broad, and their weapons light of load. Gunpowder didn't work well with their empyrean magic or traditional pragmatism. Instead, large ballistae bolts were ignited with sacred incantations, which cut through the sky in significant trails of light. Flame projectors at the front of the ships spewed thick streams of napalm, setting ablaze a few of the pirate ships.[11]

All hands were at the ready on the *Marengeld* in the ensuing chaos. The starboard cannons rang out; the templar ships were staggered and quick to evade the salvo. "The next one who misses their mark shall be buried in a tomb of coral," Algreven swore. The crew was frantic. Salerina saw only opportunity in this time as her sentry broke his concentration. She quickly turned around and grabbed ahold of his hand, struggling with the pistol he held. She was able to point it at Rodolfo's captor before he could react and shot him dead. "Grab . . . the keys. Free yourself. Then give me a hand," she said, still wrestling with her sentry.

Rodolfo quickly unlocked his shackles and ran to aid Salerina. Together they were able to overwhelm the other guard and knock him overboard into the ocean. They were on equal footing with the rest of the crew on the *Marengeld* now. Explosions and fire filled the air as the raging sea battle continued all around them. Broken ships sank in the semishallow waters off the coast. The edge of the battle began to turn against Algreven's crew. He took his sword and went to the bow of the *Marengeld* until he could feel the mist of the ocean upon his face. He swung his sword and summoned a wave, which crashed into one of the templar ships.

The *Adjudicator* had set its sights on the *Marengeld*; its flame projectors roared. However, Algreven summoned another wave, shielding the *Marengeld* as it now prepared to fire a retaliating salvo. But once the water subsided, the *Adjudicator* had changed its course. Algreven taunted Diana, but she was not fool enough to approach him while he wielded the *Tide Shifter*.

The only tide she cared about was that of the current battle, which continued to go in favor of the templar. Algreven snarled and cursed to the deep seas. He cut and slashed with his sword, creating a torrent of waves around the *Marengeld* in a blind frenzy. The water splashed and the mist grew greater until he was near drenched in water. One of the templar ships set loose its flame projectors on the water near the *Marengeld*. The liquid flame mixed with the water, creating a maelstrom of flame. Before Algreven could react, a tide of fire engulfed him. The sword dropped from his hand as he plummeted into the dichotomous maelstrom that swallowed him whole and killed him in its tumultuous foam.

The members of his crew who had not been stricken down by the templar navy or by the hands of Rodolfo or Salerina quickly surrendered. Rodolfo picked up the *Tide Shifter* and held it firmly. Now the *Adjudicator* pulled alongside the *Marengeld*. They could see Grand Admiral Diana make her way over to board the ship. The captured pirates knew her name well, and one by one, they turned their shameful gaze away with each step of her approach. Her calm demeaner and her resolute presence preceded even her glorious rank as she quickly familiarized herself with the situation aboard the *Marengeld*.

She then turned and looked at Rodolfo and Salerina. "Well, one of you doesn't seem to fit in with this crowd," she said.

"Yes, but we are together," Rodolfo said.

"And who leads who in this arrangement?" she returned.

Salerina looked at Rodolfo and gave a faint smile before turning back to face Diana. "We figure we let the situation decide for us."

Diana nodded her head. "Seems appropriate. What was your business among these pirates?"

"Trouble tends to follow us no matter where we go it seems," Salerina said. Rodolfo could do nothing but laugh at the thought.

A silence fell as Diana looked at her second-in-command before she returned her attention to the conversation. "Well, whatever the reason for you both being here, you have my thanks and the thanks of my fleet and the order. Quite the brave task you both undertook for such a weapon as that." She pointed to the *Tide Shifter*. "That will be best kept safe far away from these parts."

Salerina's eyes grew wide. "And what do we get besides kind words for the feat of recovering it?"

The templar who were going through the ship had brought a few chests to Diana in the midst of the conversation. These were filled to the brim with gild, fairy florals, pelthoms, and many other coins from around Asterra. "Well, we have little use for this. Maybe this shall make up for us taking this sword off your hands?"

Rodolfo was quite pleased, but Salerina had set her eyes on something else. "And the ship?" she said.

Diana looked at Salerina and gave a faint smile. "There will always be pirates around these shores. And it is always good to have another friendly ship along the coast. If you fancy yourself an able captain, might you be up to the task of keeping these shores safe?"

Salerina clenched her fist and shook it with enthusiasm. "What a gift. Ah, the *Marengeld*, what a beauty she is. Surely better than the sword by far. Roldy, what do you say for a quick trip?"

He laughed. "Sure, we can discuss our next adventure over lunch."

"I would like that, but you're paying," she said, looking at the chests filled with various coins.

"I can't argue with that," Rodolfo said. He looked out across the Sillian Ocean. "It's a fine day to sail."

Salerina nodded her head in agreement. "And an even better day to be a captain."

LESTER MANN AND THE
HOLLOW HEARTH

Lester could only faintly remember the last time he had smiled. And for him, maybe this was for the better. The distant memory of happiness only added to the burden of his sorrows, which had become a taxing weight in his middle age that he continually carried throughout the rustic town of Stahlt. His only respite was his trade as a handyman with a curious predilection to attempt to repair that which he almost knew he couldn't fix. The local folk knew him as an optimistic tinkerer who went from task to task creating an eclectic mixture of odd jobs that occupied most of his days and captured most of his time. Yet plain as he was perceived, there was something inimitable about Lester.

Every morning, before work, he woke early for a walk through town, keeping mostly to himself. A pooling anxiety, mixed and matched with a certain complexity, occupied his outlook, growing with every face he saw. His simple countenance, harder forged than portrayed, was gentle and inviting. Yet the townsfolk's feelings, which accompanied their perception, shared not the same affection as his. To many, he often seemed lost; he had promise without presence, view without vantage, and a conscience without constraint. His mind was different, though; not lesser by any means, but his mark within Stahlt was that of a strange fellow—an outcast. And his mannerisms only added to the townsfolk's treatment of poor Lester.

Some would say that Lester was always like this—born this way. Yet this was hardly so, for when Lester was just a boy, he had a friend, a best friend—just like we all find in our lives. This friend spoke little but followed him wherever he went with an unwavering heart and an adamant admiration that stood steady, faithful, and firm. For Lester, loyalty would take no other name but that of his dog, Pax.

The first moment was all it took to forge a lasting friendship, and surely, one can relate to such a joyous feeling as finding a true friend. When Lester felt alone, Pax brought him cheer, and Lester returned the favor: such remedies were second nature to them. And Lester and Pax went on every adventure they could find together. Within the town of Stahlt and down the Roads of Holly, there were many places to explore and many more moments to share. However, the Forest of Grent shared not the same fortune as its neighbors: it was a dark and mysterious forest, filled with an equal share of tales of wonder and tales of woe. Many had disappeared within the Forest of Grent, and stories circulated of an evil that lured lost souls into the woods, but most of these tales were created to keep children safe from the dangers that lurked in the darkness.

For this reason and many others, Lester was told by his parents that he was never to enter the Forest of Grent, and he was loyal to his word to never step foot within the foreboding woods. Yet from afar, his eyes wandered, his mind wondered, and his ears listened. He occasionally overheard a few lonely young souls of Stahlt, who felt neglected, create their own tales that spoke of enchanted groves deep within the forest that they could escape to. It was a perplexing, intriguing thought, but for Lester, he cared little for such thoughts, for he had all he wanted. And life was full and promising for him and Pax.

But seasons passed and years came and went, and while Lester grew stronger and more adventurous, poor Pax grew weaker and more lethargic; yet his heart still remained true. A passing smile from Lester would ease any pain of Pax's, and that was truly a gift no enchanted grove could conjure.

Alas, a cool winter wind began to blow, sweeping away the last hopeful chance of perennial life. And one cold day when Lester returned home, Pax was nowhere to be found.

"Mother, father," Lester desperately pleaded, "where is Pax?"

Both of his parents looked at each other with little to say. "Lester, Pax had to go away," his mother somberly said, with a look of pure sadness on her pale white face.

There was a moment of silence as Lester looked around in confusion, still unsure of what to think. "Where could he have gone? It is not like him to venture off without me by his side."

His parents knew well that Lester wouldn't understand. Lester saw the world differently than others. His was a hopeful heart, kind and brimming with a unique love that held onto a glimpse of life that his mind often seemed not to grasp. And his heart surely would break if he knew the truth—that Pax had passed away of old age. At this moment, Lester's father thought of an idea, something easier to say than the piercing truth that poor Pax would never return. "Lester, he ventured out into the Forest of Grent this morning on his walk. Like many lost souls, he is held with the spirits of the forest."

Lester closed his eyes in disbelief, releasing a pool of fresh warm tears. "Well, I will have to get him back!"

His parents looked at each other, and his mother shook her head as a single tear rolled down her left cheek. She knew her son; her Lester would never understand, and foreboding fantasies wouldn't prevent him from trying to reclaim his companion. "Grent is far too dangerous for people to venture into, and the spirits of the forest don't give souls back without reason. But maybe if you write them, they might oblige," his mother desperately said.

So Lester knew well what he had to do, and nothing in the world would convince him otherwise. From that day onward, he wrote a letter daily, and he sent them out into the Forest of Grent by way of carrier bird. He did so mostly during twilight, when the last caliginous rays of sun pierced through the thick branches of the forest, for this was when he heard the spirits were most likely to be at peace and listen. And by the edges of the forest, he would wait until his eyes grew weary, and then he would retire for the evening, waiting to repeat the same task on the following day.

For many years Lester did this, and in such time, the town of Stahlt and its people changed; children grew older, and eventually

Lester lost the comfort of his father and mother by his side. He missed them dearly, and he was alone in this cold world, and that was a sad thought indeed for such a gentle soul. The carrier birds he cared for would return from the forest every evening, but with little fortune to bring to Lester. However, he continued to write his letters despite such failures and loss, and the townsfolk painted him as a madman and wanted nothing to do with such a person. They poked fun at him and called him "lesser man"; to them, anyone that would send letters every day into the woods for no one to read surely must be far too damaged and deranged.

But maybe, just maybe, they didn't understand, and I wish I could have told Lester such a thought. For he needed to hear that his heart was far from damaged. But few would call out to him in such fervent love as he called out to Pax. And an increasingly melancholic guilt wore his expression. His eyes grew more tired than they had ever been, and the innate goodness in Lester's heart couldn't seem to come to terms with the chaos and confusion of the world, especially in Stahlt.

At times he thought to run deep into the Forest of Grent to look for Pax; there was little left in Stahlt for him anyway, and he thought it a terrible tragedy to stay somewhere where he wasn't wanted. But when he would step within the Forest of Grent, his stomach would become sick with a certain fear, and a clouding darkness would overcome him. This wasn't the way to reclaim his friend, his dear Pax; he felt it all too true, and he would retire from his journey and turn home with tears in his eyes. "I am sorry, Pax; I just can't go farther," he would say with a faint cry. "But I still won't give up looking for you." And that was all too true. Lester never gave up, no matter what troubles he endured as a result.

The town elders scoffed at his presence. "Lester Mann—what a foul look for Stahlt." The young aristocrats snickered. "There is no man lesser than Lester." And for Lester, the days felt all the same, and his work came as but a temporary distraction, perchance an attempt of somber resolution. His most recent job of fixing the hollow hearth of the town mayor's home was yet another failure. "A useless attempt," the mayor proclaimed. "Your heart is surely not in the right place—too caught up in Grent, and that is a shame."

However, a few of the young people of Stahlt were enamored by the old promising tales of Grent, and one by one, they became lost within the woods. Many townsfolk believed there was little to be done to remedy such a situation, and they carried on with their day without hesitation.

One morning the mayor's daughter went missing, and most of the townsfolk suspected she had been lost for good, like so many of the others within the forlorn forest. Commotion and talk spread among the streets and shops of Stahlt. "Another one lost to the woods," they proclaimed.

"What a pity. So young, too, with so much promise," one said.

"I don't see what one could find in such a desolate place that they couldn't find here. But if it was a remedy or peace they sought, I'm afraid such a senseless soul wouldn't have had the wit to make well of it." The others nodded their heads in agreement.

On order of the mayor, the townsfolk organized and sent out search parties, which came and went within the Forest of Grent, and soon Lester was all alone again.

One cold and windy winter night, he sent his letter into the woods as he had done time and time again, but this night he noticed that his carrier bird had taken an awfully long time to return. "Hm, it is not like Cornelius to take such time in his flight. I hope he is alright," he emphatically said, as he neared the edges of the forest and began to call out for poor Cornelius. Soon he was relieved to see the sight of his bird making its way out of the woods. However, a few passing moments later, he heard a faint sound come from within Grent, and it grew louder and more pronounced with every waking second.

At first Lester was nervous, but then he grew eager with excitement as his eyes widened and glistened with fresh tears. "Oh, maybe, oh, it must be—Pax," he said aloud, hoping his birds would chirp with a rejoicing cadence. The silhouetted figure approached, and Lester's heart cantered gracefully but soon stopped its rhythm. He looked onward and saw before him not Pax but a young woman, no older than twenty-five years of age.

She was worn and weary, and her clothes were ragged and ripped. She looked at Lester and was filled with relief. "Every day, for many months, I read your letters that were dropped on the forest floor by your birds. Such love was the only semblance of hope I held onto, and it held onto me when I needed it most. Little by little, I followed the path of your carrier birds until I soon began to see the forest's edge, but I became frightened until I found this last letter. Your devoted carrier bird dropped it by my feet and watched me until I had finished reading it, as if he wished for me to come home with him." She faintly smiled. "It is a unique hope that captures you; something surely far removed from these parts."

Lester had yet to understand the situation before him. "Did you see my dog Pax?" he said.

The girl frowned. "No, I didn't, and I am sorry for your loss, for I know you loved, and continue to love, him dearly." She paused for a moment. "When I read your letters, I pictured Pax in my mind as if I had known him better than my own self. And for a time, it must have been true, for I was lost within Grent for so long. Pax might not be with you, but I don't believe you ever lost him; your love for him has a presence of its own." She smiled. "I am Abigail, the daughter of the mayor, and I know who you are. I don't know how to thank you, but I know I shall never forget you or what you have done and continue to do," she said as she waved goodbye to Lester and continued into town.

Within one of the grand manors, within the most beautiful area of Stahlt, the mayor and his wife sat drearily in front of the cold, empty hearth, in which evanescent embers of days past congregated. The sundered stones brought in a coldness from the earth, and the hearth, unable to be lit, was dark, and the house remained still. But then a knock at the door broke through the silence, and the mayor and his wife wondered who it could be at such a late hour. When the door opened, they were delighted to see their daughter, and they embraced her warmly as fresh tears ran down their faces.

"Oh, Abigail, we thought we lost you for good," the father said.

The mother looked her daughter in the face as a certain light returned to her eyes. "How did you find your way back?"

"That man, Lester, by the woods helped me find my way home."

"Lester, that lost soul of Stahlt?" the father said in surprise and confusion.

The daughter smiled as she looked at her father with conviction. "As long as there is one good heart in the world, what can truly ever be lost?"

Word spread throughout town, and one by one the townsfolk began to look at Lester in a newfound light. They first gave greetings to Lester, and then they were soon congratulating him and cheering for him, which was a grand sight indeed. Most began to think their past behaviors ill-mannered, for what was once foolish was now not so foolish at all. And the thought of "lesser man" faded into obscurity, where it truly belonged.

On a sunny, calm-weather day, Lester went to the forest to send his letter, and many of the townsfolk gathered to listen to its message. Lester smiled, and what warmth it gave. Pax's memory graced Stahlt but now more pronounced than ever, and I shed a tear in joy for you, Lester. Some hearths require a unique fire, a burning passion of sorts, that only a certain soul can find. And Lester, when you smile, well, when you smile, everything you have ever loved, and continue to love, smiles with you. And for that, my friend, above all things, I smile, too.

CURRENCY INVESTING WITH GRIMALDO ELWIDGET

From the article "Financing Fantasies"
by Grimaldo Elwidget in the Cabel Chronicle,
April 7, 4122 A.L.Y.

Welcome to Cabel, the main financial hub of Xirtis and the place where dreams are bought and broken all in the matter of a simple breath of air. My name is Grimaldo Elwidget, but the savviest investors call me G-widge, and some of my lesser-than-lucky clients call me Grim or Grimy—but I don't let that dampen my day. Heck, they're still my clients, after all, and they still realize more gains with me than they would with any other broker. I am an optimistic investor—what we call an ox in this market—and everyone knows I have big plans. Don't let my size fool you: this half gnome, half q'zardi handles some of the biggest currency transactions in all of Asterra for some of the wealthiest clients this side of the Euyril River.

Now, there are a lot of moving parts to any market in Asterra, and with the currency exchange, this applies tenfold. There are hundreds of different currencies within Asterra, and I deal with all of them, but for this article, just mentioning five of the most prominent and most traded currencies should do the trick in giving you an introduction to how the magic works. And when you know more, you lose less— unless you are just unlucky, and then I can't help you.

Anyway, let's get started; these free consultations don't put food on my table. The first currency is the one I often find myself trading

more than any other, and it is for good reason: it is what I like to call the gold, or gild, standard. Gild is the main currency found within the realms of man, and even within most other realms. It is by far the most popular currency in all of Asterra, and as such, it is the most traded and most established. For this reason, it is the base currency for which all other currencies are measured, owing its success to the strength and stability of many of the eastern realms of man. If you want to start off in the currency market, you can never go wrong with investing in gild.

The second most used currency is the pelthom, which just so happens to get its name from the Old Dwarvish word for money, or so I am told. This fancy coin has seen much success in recent years due to the rekindled strength of the dwarven realm under King Danemere. It's not cheap, with just 1 pelthom equaling 1.8 gild. However, dwarven goods have been in high demand due to their increasing quality, and the currency has been readily adopted as a steady alternative in some human realms. So may I say, I am quite "oxish" on it as an investment. And I wouldn't lie—I have my seven children's portfolios invested in it.

Next up is the elvish lumna, which for a long time was almost equal to the value of gild. However, some of the elvish realms have seen a rise in interest rates, which has increased the value of 1 lumna to equal 1.19 gild.[12] My prediction is that this little greenish coin will continue to slowly rise over the next few months. Seems the elvish council has done something right recently.

The last two coins are quite unique, but are still well-known enough to most currency traders. The first is the fairy floral, which is the main currency used by—you guessed it—fairies. These coins are found throughout all of the fairy realms and even in most of the elvish realms as an alternate currency. The value of the floral is 1 to 0.8 gild, as it has been slightly devalued due to a series of scandals within the fairy realms.

Now, I am quite "wolfish"—or what one might call pessimistic—on this last one, but if you are looking for some cheap goods that will degrade faster than an overcooked ham, look no further than the orcish galka. Since orcs have a well-known tempestuous temperament—to put it nicely—the galka has seen a strong decline in its value, pricing it at 1 to 0.42 gild and leading orcish goods to be quite the cheap alternative. Now, you may ask, what does orcish temperament have to do with their currency losing value? Well, orcs have recently developed a bad habit of killing some of their creditors, and with such a poor reputation, they haven't been able to find new credit sources—shocking, I know. Well, the creditors lucky enough to escape the axe still have collections on orcish accounts, and there doesn't seem to be any way for the orcs to reconsolidate their debt.[13]

I still see many fellow brokers that are quite oxish on the galka here in the exchange market, but I tell you, that coin ain't rebounding anytime soon. And speaking of time, you must know that the exchange market is open five days a week. What happens on the other two days? Mail, to put it simply—lots and lots of mail from clients. And if you want to be on the top and stay pace with the market trends, you best invest in at least one peregrine falcon to deliver your messages.[14] Heck, I have eight at my disposal: Tirmin, Geldur, Baldin, Hurin, Alzaris, Filliarella, Seliria, and Steve; the last one is a family name. Anyhow, this will ensure that your message gets to where it needs to go in record time.

Once I receive my clients' mail, I start getting ready to process their orders before the market opens. Most of the time, I send the readied orders by mail, but other times I am right here in the exchange—or the temple, as I like to call it. Here, all the banks exchange currency, and of course, there are many other players, including us brokers.

The most pivotal bit of info when trading money is that these trades are always, as we like to call it, dynamic duos—that is, two items change hands, which is why all prices are relative.[15] And there are many ways you can invest in this market, and I often engage in every form of investment type. Some brokers' clients are a bit squeamish when it comes to futures or options,[16] but I tell my clients that if they want to make money, they need to take some major risks; however, there really aren't any risks when investing with me. Heck,

Michael Frank Rizzo

one of my clients, an elvish wandmaker from Emberdell, has more than decupled his initial investment by taking my advice.

That is what can happen when you learn a bit of my mindset. Losses don't phase me—if I have any at all on a given day—and they shouldn't phase you either. In fact, I mostly say that hedging is for cowards. I mean, if you go into any transaction fearing a loss, you are just going to create one, aren't you? However, when you are in the business as long as I've been, you start to find out most customers become a bit apprehensive to use a broker who doesn't plan for the worst. So, I do hedge my positions, but I assure you it is often not necessary when trading with G-widge. I mean, who needs a stop-loss when your spots are just spot on?[17]

Every market has its major players, and I just so happen to be one of the stars here in Cabel. Now, there are hundreds of currency exchange markets all throughout Asterra. Some of these focus on the lesser-known currencies. But like I said before, Cabel is the pinnacle of investment, and it is where the magic truly happens. And I am its grand wizard. So, really, the only question you have to ask yourself is—are you ready to make yourself rich with G-widge?

Four for Pillacella

Elpern looked down at the invitation he held in his hand for what seemed like the one-hundredth time. *Come, friends, to help Berdribrul celebrate her 50th birthday,* he read in his head. Elpern could taste the cake and see the familiar faces with every step forward along the forest path. He pictured dwarves, fairies, elves, nuffi, melrins, q'zardi, esterelians, and many others playing wondrous games and singing merry songs. It would be the party of the year, and he couldn't be any more excited.

Alongside him, his good friend Alzamos, a nimble q'zardi, groomed his olive-colored fur, tidied his small coat, and checked his pocket watch. "Quite the pleasant stroll," he cheerily said.

"Yes, this area of the woods is far nicer than anywhere I've been recently," Elpern returned. The fine deciduous trees that outlined the forest path towered above them, creating a lush, verdant shroud of leaves. The patches of sun, which pierced through the forest ceiling, revealed various critters and birds that filled the forest with peaceful ambient sounds.

Elpern and Alzamos were quite relaxed on their journey, but their friend, Tüvlin the dwarf, rubbed the back of his neck unenthusiastically. "Why would Sindil decide to move all the way out here? Everyone knows all the well-to-do, not how-do-you-do, elves live in these parts of the woods. I much preferred the look of Abbey Pine," Tüvlin said, as he trudged his small dwarven legs along the winding woodsy road.

It wasn't the first complaint heard from Tüvlin along their journey, and from the look of Elpern, it wouldn't be the last. "It's just up ahead; it shan't be much longer," Elpern said.

Tüvlin sighed. "Okay, okay, well, we must hurry because we still need to buy a proper gift for Berdribrul."

"Don't worry, I know exactly what we will bring to the party. It'll be a nice gift from us all," Alzamos said.

Tüvlin's eyes opened wide. "Just one gift from four people?"

"Yes, but it'll be fine. It is a proper gift—quite a good one actually."

Tüvlin shrugged. Elpern patted him on the back. "You must stop worrying. You think far too much. See"—he pointed up ahead down the winding road—"there is the sign for Glen Hollow. Sindil's house should be coming up."

They entered the small pristine village and were greeted with only the small sounds of the tame woods. The first house they passed was a large cottage-style mansion with at least three chimneys. The second house was on a plot of land that could have fit ten more houses its own size. Then there was Sindil's house, smaller than most of the rest but still quite large in size and moderately lavish in appearance. There were two towers, one on each frontal side of the house, that waved slightly back and forth to their peak, a design that was quite customary for eloquent elvish architecture. The roof had slight undulations that accentuated the spaces that many large windows filled.

"Not bad for a wandmaker from Abbey Pine, ey?" Alzamos said with a smirk.

When they arrived at the front door, Sindil was already waiting for them. He opened it wide and greeted them with a large smile. "Not bad for an elvish wandmaker, right?" he said in similar fashion.

Tüvlin's large dwarven eyes glimmered at the gold décor. "How were you able to afford all of this . . . I'm sorry, don't mean to pry; it reminds a dwarf of the mines of Dwathrin," he said.

Sindil brushed it off with an energetic wave of his hand. "Don't be silly, Tüvlin; we're all friends here. I gave a good chunk of my savings to that fellow Grimaldo Elwidget at the Xirtis Currency Exchange in Cabel. It was a risk, but you know me; anyway, he sure knows what he's doing. Now, are you all coming in or what?"

"Not sure how much time we have to spare," Alzamos said.

"Not to worry, I'll just be a minute. Come in. Don't wait outside." Sindil disappeared for what seemed like almost ten minutes, and when he reappeared, he was dressed lavishly in a new tunic and fine clothes. "See, quick," he said. He rubbed Alzamos's furry head as they left the house. "Quite the coat you have grown since I have last seen you, my friend. Must be the best looking q'zardi[18] this side of the Windyrose River." He quickly looked at Elpern. "And you must have grown to be the tallest esterelian I know, Elpern. And your anxious ways haven't escaped you, Tüvlin," he said with a smile. "Now are we ready for this party?"

"Well, we still need to get a gift for Berdribrul before anything else," Elpern said.

"Oh, and what have we decided on?" Sindil said cheerily.

"Yes, I thought that we should buy a nice bottle of oak rose wine. It is a delicious and smooth treat, and Berdribrul will surely enjoy it," Alzamos said.

Elpern nodded. "Ah, that is a great choice."

"No, no, no, that will not do at all," Sindil said. He pointed his finger in the air and then shook it in the direction of the group. "I know just what melrins enjoy, especially one with such exquisite taste as Berdribrul."

The rest of them looked at each other. "Well, what is it then?" Tüvlin inquired.

Sindil smiled. "Pillacella liquor, of course. It is the most luxurious after-dinner drink, and one that will surely make quite the hit at the party."

"Will Bernardibus have it in his shop?" Alzamos said.

"No, not a chance, this is a rare liquor; but don't worry I know just the person and the place that will have it in stock. We will just have to go to Ayramar."

Tüvlin almost stopped in his tracks. "But that is almost due north, and we have to travel westward. We don't have the time."

Alzamos looked at his pocket watch. "Yes, Tüvlin's right, it is already a quarter to five, and the party starts at six; we will surely be late."

Sindil calmly motioned with his hands. "Believe me, it will be worth being a few minutes late for this. Besides, I know a shortcut. We'll be at my friend Nulwill's shop in no time, and then we'll head straight for the party. It'll be a nice trip; I promise," he said.

The rest of them looked at each other in dubious silence. "Alright, let's do it. It has been some time since we all have been on an adventure together," Elpern said, with a bit of reluctance.

"Good, and what about you two?" Sindil said, looking at Tüvlin and Alzamos. Alzamos reluctantly agreed. Tüvlin had no choice but to sigh and agree to go along as well.

At the next crossroads, instead of following the path that led to Berdribrul's house, they took the opposite route towards Ayramar. The woods grew thicker and the road became far more rustic only a few hundred paces along their new course. But Sindil was ever sure and ever confident that they would soon be at their destination. "Alright, this is where we abandon the road and walk through the forest; it should cut our journey in half."

Tüvlin took one look at the thick dark woods and then turned his glance to Sindil. "Are you crazy? Dwarves and forests don't go well together."

"It doesn't look like the most stable path," Alzamos said. "Are you sure you know where you're going, Sindil?"

"We can take the path and go around, but it will take us almost twice as long, and time is of the essence. Don't worry. Old Sindil here knows these forests better than the wands he makes," Sindil said. Tüvlin subtly scoffed at the thought.

Elpern took the first step off the path. "I am the largest among us. I'll lead, just in case the inhabitants get unruly." His large esterelian frame eclipsed both Tüvlin and Alzamos, who followed close behind. Sindil was the last to enter the woods but continued to bark orders from behind the pack.

As they abandoned the sight of the trail behind them, the trees grew larger and the air filled with a strange, earthy odor. Tüvlin covered his distinguished dwarven nose. "It smells like garbage drenched in bog water."

Alzamos raised his voice. "It isn't me; I shampooed my fur thoroughly this morning," he said in the shadow of Elpern.

"No, no, the whole forest reeks of something foul," Elpern said, curiously looking around but finding nothing to explain such a stench.

There was a small thud along the forest floor. Tüvlin looked around but couldn't see anything moving around in the woods. However, he could feel something along his right leg. Before he could look down to see what it was, he was swept off his feet, and whatever it was slowly began dragging him along the forest floor. His head jolted and frantically shook, but when he could stabilize his neck, he managed to catch a glimpse of a long stalk-like vine leading off farther into the woods. He tried to yell for help at first, but he was still trying to catch his breath. He managed to muster a bit of air in his lungs. "Get this beast off me!"

Elpern, Sindil, and Alzamos were already working on trying to free Tüvlin. But they soon noticed that what dragged their dwarven friend along the forest was no beast but rather bridle bristle twine. Its large bulbous aperture, which its many vines were connected to, revealed a bevy of sharp teeth-like thorns, and its many vines, branching out from the central head, created a nightmarish maelstrom of chaos. Tüvlin was getting dragged ever closer, and if something wasn't done quickly, he would be plant food.

"What is taking so long?" he cried aloud. "By Dæmar's Forge, try anything," he yelled. He was near the source of the garbage-bog scent; whatever the plant last ate, and the digestive chemical processes that had ensued, almost knocked Tüvlin out cold. *Maybe this was for the best though,* he thought; it seemed like there was nothing to be done. He surely couldn't escape on his own, and his friends hadn't done much but delay his captor's meal. He looked in dismay at Alzamos and Sindil, pulling with all of their might. *Wait, where is Elpern?*

The large-bodied esterelian had another plan. He had seen a large branch on the ground. With all of his strength, he now wielded it like a large club and dealt a massive blow to the bulbous head of the plant. It recoiled and loosened its grip on Tüvlin; its other stalk-like vines moved steadily back to attack. Elpern took another swing at the plant. "Grab Tüvlin and make a run for it," he yelled to Alzamos and Sindil. "I will follow right behind."

They didn't think twice. They quickly pulled Tüvlin up from the ground; normally the dwarf would say something about such treatment, but he was thankful just to leave the woods as quickly as possible.

When they were almost out of reach of the plant, Alzamos waved to Elpern, who started to run to safety. "Hurry, you can make it," he shouted in angst. The vines were slow though, and Elpern was able to rejoin the group. Alzamos patted Elpern's kneecap; it was about the farthest up the esterelian he could reach. "Great job; you sure bested it."

Tüvlin was still catching his breath, but he was also being a slight bit dramatic. Sindil stared confusedly into the woods and scratched his head. "Hmm, normally bridle bristle twine isn't found in these parts. I guess we will just have to try and find another way."

All of a sudden it seemed Tüvlin had reclaimed his lost energy. "You almost got me killed, and this is how you act?" He fumed with rage. "I think we should just go with our original plan."

Elpern and Alzamos seemed to agree, but Sindil was convincing, or at least very adamant. "We came all this way, and surely we have seen the worst of what is in store for this journey; we can get back to the road and follow the path to Nulwill's. If we quicken our pace, we can make up for lost time and then follow the road southwest to Berdribrul's." He stared at them, not breaking his gaze for even a fraction of a second. "Come on," he walked over to Tüvlin. "Pal, I am sorry. You know I would never want to see you get hurt, or eaten, but we had some crazy adventures in our youth, and this wouldn't be the first time we've faced danger before, right?" He looked at the rest of the group.

"Yeah, but for a fancy drink?" Tüvlin said.

"Not any fancy drink—pillacella," Sindil protested. "And, I never said anything when I was asked to go on countless journeys to the likes of places I wouldn't dare go again. We can't forget Stonefel Pass, can we?"

The others shuddered. "Alright, how much farther is it?" Alzamos said.

Sindil gave a subtle grin. "Not too much farther, I promise. And it will be worth it."

Tüvlin couldn't help but sigh. He knew that once Sindil set his mind on something, he simply just had to have it. And with his new-found money, the possibilities for misfortune seemed to be endless. "Let's just make it back to the road intact. I'll be much happier then; dwarves do not like the woods," he reiterated to the group.

They made it back to the road in little time and were on their way to retrieve the fabled pillacella that Sindil couldn't stop praising. "Alzamos, how has Elemea been?" Elpern asked, desperately trying to refocus the conversation on something other than Sindil's lavish tastes.

Alzamos happily nodded and smiled. Not an inch of his proper attire moved out of place. "She is doing splendid. She took the kids to her mother's house for the weekend to go on some of their own adventures."

Elpern gave a mischievous smile. "Ah, so you have the house all to yourself for the whole weekend. Looking to throw an after-party, Alzy?" Alzamos hadn't even considered that an option. Elpern was quite the socialite. He was the king of every cocktail hour and had devised his very own system of securing hors d'oeuvres. Alzamos, on the other hand, was content with his collection of elvish and q'zardi fairytales along with his steam pipe.

"I have much reading to catch up on," he said.

"It's a missed opportunity, Alzy. I'm telling you; you'll regret not taking advantage of it."

Alzamos waved his hand carelessly and facetiously in the direction of Elpern. "Milerna will be worried sick if you are out partying too late, again." He laughed a bit.

"She'd rather have me out of the house for a bit. Believe me," Elpern said. "If anyone is doing it right, it might as well be you, Tüvlin."

Tüvlin was beyond surprised. "How so?"

"All you have to answer to is Ruffil. How is the little rascal?"

Tüvlin gave a warm smile. It was the first time along the journey he had done so. "Better than ever, and I should be there to keep him company. I have the neighbors watching him this evening so he doesn't get lonely."

Sindil snickered. "Actually, if there is one of us that is doing it right, it is that dog." The rest of them laughed, with the exception of Tüvlin. But their laughs didn't last too long. Tüvlin turned around and gave them a stern look. And he was quite shocked how quickly they quieted, and how still they stood. *It's about time I receive a bit of respect*, he thought to himself. However, when he turned around, he joined them in shock.

Before them was a woodland troll, standing directly in the middle of the road, blocking their path forward. It snarled and showed its mouth full of razor-sharp teeth. Though not as large and fierce as the other common types of trolls, it still stood about a foot taller than Elpern. Its bristly fur was a sylvan brownish-gray, and based on its heavy breathing and flaring nostrils, its patience seemed to be in limited supply.

The troll slowly approached them. "Why are you crossing my roads?"

Tüvlin might not have been the bravest dwarf, but he felt he had to point out the obvious. "I don't believe these roads belong to anyone."

The troll snarled. "Just the same as all the other travelers. Always trespassing and walking up and down my roads, making loud noises. How can one relax?"

Elpern subtly nodded. The only thing worse than a troll was a moody troll. "Well, Mr. . . ." He paused as he wasn't exactly sure how to address the troll. "We have a party to attend. And we are terribly sorry for interrupting your peaceful relaxation, but we're already running late. Is there a way we can make it up to you, so that we may be on our way?"

The troll didn't hesitate. "I need a good riddle so that I can stop adventurers from passing on my roads. That will put an end to this mischief."

Alzamos was confused. For the first time today, he absentmindedly messed up his fur with a flurry of puzzled scratches. "Well, aren't you doing just th—"

Before he could finish his sentence, Sindil hit him in the side with his elbow. "Of course, everyone needs a good riddle. We know quite a lot of them." Sindil gave a convincing glance to the rest of the group.

He was quite good at planting an idea into someone's head; he had the conviction for it.

Elpern nodded. "Yes, of course, I have learned many riddles in my time." Elpern wasn't as convincing at lying as Sindil, but he had an amicable enough personality to pull it off. He stood there thinking for a few minutes.

The troll grew more impatient. It was ready to say something when Elpern spoke up. "I have a good one for you," he said with a bit of excitement and pride in his voice. "Ready?" The troll snarled as it towered over the group, staring at Elpern with its piercing gaze. "Okay, here it is:

Two's a pair
But one's to eat
The other to wear
A travel and treat
With neither spelt the same
Can you guess their common sounding name?"

The troll grimaced. The group couldn't tell if it was thinking or if it was ready to send them back the way they came. It massaged its facial fur and let out a snuffle. "This won't do."

Elpern seemed rather upset, even offended by some extent. "Why not? It is a good riddle," he protested.

"The structure is poor." Elpern grew even more visibly upset. "Besides, the answer is shoe or choux, whichever you choose. A play on pastry by someone who has their mind on food and feet in use; not the best for stopping a wandering traveler. I'll give you one more try." The troll grimaced at them.

It was true. Elpern hadn't stopped thinking about cake since the moment they had embarked for Sindil's house. And anything he could think of had to do with food or travel.

Tüvlin politely raised his stubby hand, as if he waited to be asked to participate. The troll looked at him, which was more than enough of a sign for him to proceed. "I believe I might have one." He let out a deep breath. "Here goes nothing," he whispered.

"Drink till you drop
Always the last you spot
Yet it'll stay in sight
Lest you peer to the right
'Tis sinister yet sweet
What drink's a treat?"

The troll didn't say a word; it didn't even move an inch. It was deep in thought. Tüvlin was well-mannered enough to raise his hand again. "Would you like a hint?"

The troll grinned, but shook its head in approval. "This riddle is sure to stump those pesky adventurers who are always disturbing my rest," the troll said. "I don't know; is the answer rum?"

Tüvlin smiled for the second time. "I'm afraid not. The answer was port wine. Get it?" he said. "Strong drink—drink till you drop. Port—left. Left side—sinister side. Sweet after-dinner drink. Not bad, huh?"

Elpern lightly patted Tüvlin on the shoulder. "I think it gets it, now," he politely whispered.

The troll nodded its head slightly. "Yes, this is just what I can use to guard my roads." It slowly moved away from the middle of the road. "You can pass. By the way, it is Mr. Irburrow—Firn Irburrow," the troll said, looking at Elpern.

"You have our thanks, Mr. Irburrow," Elpern said. He couldn't help but think that it was an odd name for a troll as the sight of Firn faded into the background.

There was an awkward silence among the group of four as they continued on with their journey. Sindil couldn't be sure, but he had a sneaky suspicion they were angry with him. "Isn't it nice that all four of us are adventuring again?" he said cheerily.

Tüvlin grimaced. "Can't wait to see what else is in store for us," he said sarcastically.

Sindil was shocked. "Look, I just thought it would be nice to relive a bit of the adventuring days of old before the party—possibly catch up a bit and rely a bit on serendipity to add some excitement to our path forward."

Alzamos looked at his pocket watch and shook his head. "I don't think it has been playing in our favor so far." He closed his watch and put it away with a sigh. Q'zardi never liked being late. They were usually the first to arrive at parties.

Sindil shook his head. For the first time that day, he felt quite bad. And the rest of the group weren't too happy to see his cheery personality fade away. Despite their recent troubles, the rest knew Sindil always meant well and was just excited to see his friends; though, he had a unique way of showing it.

Tüvlin was about to apologize, but there was little need. A familiar sight came into view and Sindil's spirits quickly lifted up. "Ah, there it is," he said. "Ayramar is up ahead." He pointed at the sign ahead. "Nulwill's shop is right on the outskirts." They walked towards the small village hidden within the woods. Ayramar was a place they all had heard about, but none of them, save Sindil, had been.

And from the looks of it, they could understand why. There was nothing around, with the exception of a few cottages, an inn, a small market, a town center, and a few other scattered buildings. And there, of course, was Nulwill's small shop that doubled as his home. They entered without hesitation and were greeted to a small old-world store that was filled with an eclectic mixture of spirits and mysterious brews. The variegated colors of the myriad of different bottles glimmered in the faint candle-light. And towards the back of the store, stacking a few bottles on one of the crowded shelves, was a thin elder elf. Sindil drew a big smile on his face. "Ah, Nulwill," Sindil said enthusiastically, "good to see you, old pal."

Nulwill turned around and patted the dust off his elvish blazer and slicked back what remained of his thin elvish hair. "Sindil, I am glad to see you. It has been a few weeks since we last exchanged letters."

"Yes, yes. I almost have a bad habit of losing track of time." Alzamos gave Sindil a bewildered look. "You still have some of that pillacella you were telling me about?" Sindil asked.

Nulwill smiled. "It has been going fast, but you know I would never give it all away without stashing at least one bottle for you,

Sindil." He moved his lanky legs over to the fancy liquor cabinet that decorated a small portion of the back wall of the shop. Unlocking it with a worn brass key, he fuddled through a few of the bottles and reached for a small lever, which parted the cabinet in two, revealing a hidden stash of special wines and liquors. "Ah, here we go; only the finest bottle of pillacella for you, Sindil."

"Thank you very kindly, Nulwill." Sindil proceeded to take out his embroidered elvish wallet.

The rest of the group collectively reached for their own money pouches and wallets. "How much is the total?" Tüvlin asked.

"This bottle right here is three-hundred-and-ninety lumna," Nulwill said.

Tüvlin's jaw nearly dropped; Alzamos's heart nearly stopped; Elpern nearly choked on his own saliva. "Do you have any less expensive bottles of pillacella?" Tüvlin pleaded.

"I'm afraid not. But this is one of the best you will find. It has been aged perfectly and contains only the finest fermented pilas cane."

Tüvlin could barely contribute to such a hefty gift. He was a simple woodworker, and it didn't make it any easier that elvish currency and goods were on the rise.

Sindil stepped forward. "Not to worry," he said nonchalantly. "I will pay for it in full. It is the least I can do after all the trouble that has been caused on the way here."

"No, no, we won't have it," Alzamos protested.

"Yes, it wouldn't be fair to have you do such a thing," Elpern added.

Tüvlin shook his head furiously. "Yes, we must give you something."

"I insist," Sindil said. He put the money on the table. "What else can the money be good for? And I must contribute to the journey. And I won't do this any other way," he said.

The group knew Sindil wouldn't change his mind: he was the most stubborn elf they knew.

With the transaction complete, they said their farewells to Nulwill and left the shop with the fancy bottle of pillacella.

"What does it taste like?" Elpern asked as they left Ayramar and continued down the southwest road to Berdribrul's house.

"Not really sure," Sindil said curiously. "I have had it only a couple of times, and it was many years ago."

Elpern raised his scale-like eyebrows. He was about to say something, but Tüvlin beat him to it. "You don't remember?"

"Only faintly, but trust me, it is very good. Berdribrul will love it."

"I'll take your word for it," Alzamos said. "Nothing we could change about it anyhow." He looked at his pocket watch. "We are already over an hour late. How much longer do you think we have?"

Sindil calmly waved his hand up in the air as if he were shooing off all of their collective problems. "Shouldn't be longer than fifteen minutes. And we are moving in style now. This is one of the most scenic and peaceful roads in Emberdell."

They passed by a large grouping of overgrown ferns. All of a sudden, there was a large rustling noise, followed by a fellow elf, who jumped out onto the road. "Give me all of your money," he yelled.

The group stood still. Elpern was a bit agitated that he was missing all of the festivities. Alzamos was ashamed that they would be beyond tardy. Tüvlin had passed the point of anxiety and wasn't the least bit surprised about their ongoing troubles. And Sindil was wondering if maybe his directions could use a bit of work in the future.

They all outnumbered the thief four-to-one, but the strange elf held in his hand an enchanted elvish wand from the looks of it. Wands weren't necessary for casting spells, but they could significantly aid the caster by acting as an enchanted conduit, and elvish wands were known for their quality and potency. And from his jittery composure and expression, the thief seemed to be rather on edge and looked willing to use the wand if given the chance. So they all reached into their money pouches and rummaged for their coin. Tüvlin held forty-five lumna; Elpern fashioned fifty lumna; Alzamos revealed seventy-two lumna; and Sindil produced ten lumna.

Alzamos collected up all of the coin and handed it over to the robber, at which the robber grimaced. "This is it?" He looked specifically at Sindil. "What kind of self-respecting elf walks out with only ten lumna on him?"

Elpern, Alzamos, and Tüvlin looked at Sindil as well. If he didn't give all of his money away to purchase such an expensive bottle of liquor, they probably would have been able to get past the thief. But the thief was not intending to let them go without more of a toll. "Give me your jewelry and other valuables," he said waving his wand at them. The group looked away from Sindil and sighed.

"How about this fine bottle of pillacella?" Sindil said.

"No thanks, I don't drink," the robber said. "Quickly, other valuables." He waved his wand again at the group.

While they were rummaging about for any items of worth, there was another rustle in the bushes, but it was much more prominent this time around. Soon, out from the ferns on the opposite side of the road, emerged the troll, Mr. Firn Irburrow. He was somewhat pleased to see Elpern, Alzamos, Sindil, and Tüvlin but not so pleased to find a strange trespasser on his roads.

"Who are you and what are you doing causing all of this commotion on my roads?" Firn asked.

The robber turned to Firn, holding his wand steady on the group. "What does it matter to you?" he said.

"You have disturbed my peace. And I won't let you pass unless you answer a riddle." Firn then gratefully gave a subtle nod in the direction of Tüvlin.

Tüvlin tried to shake his head to discourage the troll's attempt at the riddle. The robber was confused. "A what?"

Firn didn't listen to him before proceeding:

> "Drink till you drop
> Always the last you spot
> Yet it'll stay in sight
> Lest you peer to the right
> 'Tis sinister yet sweet
> What drink's a treat?"

The robber was having none of it. He now turned his wand towards Firn. He planned to cast a spell, but the wand seemed to be having an issuing with channeling the required energy.

As the thief curiously looked at his wand and anxiously waited for his spell to cast, Elpern saw an opportunity. As a few malfunctioning sparks erupted from the thief's wand in a colorful spectacle, Elpern charged the thief and punched him square in the face, knocking him out.

Firn shrugged his large troll shoulders. "Hmm, I guess he isn't a fan of riddles. It might work on the next traveler though?" he said, phrasing his statement almost like a question.

Sindil nodded in agreement. "Yes, I think you are right. He was just not well-mannered."

Firn snorted. "So I thought. Well, good day, friends. Hope to see you again soon," he said. The group gave their farewells to Firn before he made his way back into the woods.

Alzamos let out a sigh of relief. "We all were lucky that wand didn't work."

Elpern looked down at the wand, which lay on the forest road near the passed-out robber, and saw Sindil's seal. "This seems to be one of your wands, Sindil."

Tüvlin lightly snickered. "No surprise that it malfunctioned." The rest of them laughed, with the exception of Sindil.

Finally, about a quarter past eight, they arrived at Berdribrul's house. She opened the door and gave each of them a great big hug with her furry melrin arms. "I am so glad to see you all. I thought you weren't going to show," she said excitedly.

Sindil gave a great big smile and proceeded to hand over the bottle of pillacella. "Happy birthday, Berdribrul. This is a little gift from all of us."

"Oh, how wonderful, what is it?"

Sindil proudly looked at his friends before turning back to Berdribrul. "It is a perfectly aged bottle of pillacella."

"Wow, that is quite rare. But you didn't have to go through such trouble; I'd much prefer a nice bottle of oak rose wine."

Elpern, Alzamos, and Tüvlin all looked at each other in shock. They had no idea what to make of the whole situation. In fact, they weren't sure if they had just heard Berdribrul correctly. But they knew they weren't delirious, and they could barely muster a single collective word to say. Sindil had ventured off in such time to find refuge near the assorted pastries and cheesecakes.

Berdribrul took the initiative to break the silence. "Well, I thank you all. Now, come on in and enjoy the festivities. We were just about to cut the cake and then proceed on with the party games."

The house was packed with fairies, nuffi, elves, dwarves, melrins, q'zardi, esterelians, and many more. Persax from the Fantastical Fair Association of Trisden was there as well as Mayor Elberi from Faeril. Even Grimaldo Elwidget was in attendance.

"This is quite the party," Tüvlin said.

"Aren't you glad you didn't decide to stay home?" Elpern returned.

"Yes, but I do not wish to stay out too late," Tüvlin said, almost retreating back to his usual ways.

Sindil had made his way back from his extended trip to the dessert table and waved his hand in the air. "Don't worry, I know a secret route to get us home after the party." They all looked at each other and took a glass of the pillacella that Berdribrul had just poured.

"Let's just enjoy the party for now," Elpern said. And the group had a good laugh and were merry along with the rest of the party guests.

A Templar's Hymn

Prīma diēs certē meī vītā cōnsciā eram potuī,
In nōn spērō nāscī praebere dēbitō amōre.
Nummō tam similī numerāvī deinde diēs meī,
Quae colligēbantur nē impendēbantur at inde,
Tālis egeō dōnātae donum consequī honōrī.
Terrās fortiter inter mīrās fēcī iter omnēs,
Et pretiī invēnī gāzās multās tibi magnās;
Mentī quae at fortūnae dulcēs ōlim errant meī,
Vīsae sunt coacēscere quam mox ante oculōs meī.
Sum factus āmissus meī īnpropriō heu studiō tam,
Sūmens infortūnium iam et redeō prō dōmō.
Ēn ego indagator nōn videor minor āb tē.[19]

The first day of my conscious life, I was certainly born in debt to a love I could never hope to afford. Therefore, I counted my days so much like coin, which were gathered but then not spent in need to attain a gift for such bestowed honor. I bravely traveled amongst all the majestic lands, and I discovered many great treasures of worth for you; but the fortunes, which were once sweet to my mind, very soon seemed to sour before my eyes. Alas, I became so lost in my own pursuit, and I return in front of home claiming only disappointment. Though I, the seeker, was seen no lesser a being by you.

A Friendly Farewell

Here we are, friends, at the end of our journey throughout Asterra. We have met many people, and through their tales, we have witnessed life-altering events and discovered many secrets. Was there a particular tale or character that spoke to you? Was there something special you discovered or now one day wish to discover? Don't fret if you can't choose; you don't have to tell me at this moment!

There is much to reflect on, but for now, all I hope, above all else, is that you have enjoyed our time together just as much as I have. The joy of Asterra is always found in its people and places, which you are now a part of. I am happy that we were able to cross paths, and I know, well within my heart, we are destined to cross paths again. And until that time, I wish you will try to always look at life in wonderment of its blessings. And when I find you again, I hope you are the better for each passing day's journey upon your path.

For now, I plan to travel to Aurora, as I hear their harvest festival is about to start, and there will be many unique characters and tales to find. May the light of Asterra ease your burdens and guide you ever forward towards peace. Happy traveling!

Your friend, truly,
Penniforth Octavius Rodgers

APPENDIX OF MAGIC

A big thank you to my magical friend Callia Desil for helping me learn a bit about the basics of magic. I did my best to summarize what I learned, and I compiled the information below as a reference tool.

THE FOUR ESSENTIALS OF MAGIC[20]

1. **All magic is created out of life energy—also known as material energy. All matter contains this life/material energy, which is further broken down into essential and supplemental energy.**

    a. Life energy is the source for magical power. Life energy is found in all living things and even in objects (all matter). Magical power is created by magical beings/objects due to the magical properties/potency within the being/object, which converts life energy to magical power.

    b. When a magical object is being used by a mage, that mage uses the object's magical power that is produced from its magical properties to enhance their spellcasting capabilities.

    c. When energy is drained from a source, the user siphons the host's life energy directly but is not able to absorb magical properties/potency. As such, a user cannot learn or absorb a magical quality from another being. They can only absorb the energy to use in creating their own magical power.

    d. When an object is siphoned of its energy, the object loses the energy used to naturally create its magical properties. It is stripped of its very ethos, causing detrimental damage to the object or—light forbid—being. For this reason, siphoning is very frowned upon or, in the latter case, forbidden.

2. Life/material energy is classified as either essential energy (mental, spiritual, or incorporeal) or supplemental energy (physical), both of which are converted into magical power for spellcasting. In order to increase the frequency and potency of casting spells, it is necessary for all mages to increase their tolerance to the taxing effects of spellcasting.

   a. Living things are the greatest source of essential/spiritual energy; nonliving objects only have a miniscule amount of essential energy and mostly contain physical/supplemental energy. The essential energy of an object is often hidden and too small to reliably make an impact on spellcasting.

   b. Energy for spellcasting can be better allocated by either increasing tolerance for spellcasting or gathering energy from an external source. The former is the more efficient way to cast spells.

   c. Essential energy is the energy of incorporeal thought, spiritual presence, and intangible force and lends itself greatly to spellcasting; physical energy is that of tangible motion and action and must be reallocated from its proper designation to supplement casting.

3. A certain mental state must be achieved and maintained in order to cast spells.

4. Wands and staffs are not necessary to cast spells but can help.

   a. Wands and staffs are meant to act as conduits of energy and are usually not used for drawing energy—this is done so as not to impede the flow of magic. The storing of additional energy in a wand/staff can create a very powerful magical instrument, but this also increases the risk of malfunction, thus making said instrument dangerous for the user.

   b. Wands and staffs are made from various magical materials. Depending on the materials, each wand infuses the magic that passes through it with a unique essence. For example, a staff made from a magical root will infuse the magic performed with sylvan properties, regardless of whether the spell belongs to the sylvan branch or not. Furthermore, this means the aforementioned staff would be better used for performing sylvan spells.

Glossary

Abbey Pine: A humble town located near the Wilder Woods in Emberdell.

Algreven Lockjaw: An infamous pirate captain who was betrayed by his crew and swept off by the tides of the Sillian Ocean only to be rescued and brought to prominence among the local thieves and scoundrels of the Fire Islands. He was known as the wielder of the true-forged blade *Tide Shifter*.

Al' Fer's Bay: A beautiful inlet that connects the city of Zeris to the Idyll Sea.

Aljamer-Röner: Literally meaning "silver gemstone" in Old Dwarvish, this gemstone is found in many mines throughout the dwarven realm and is also scattered in caves, groves, and dungeons throughout Asterra. The gem's greatest value is the light it provides in dark places due to a chemical process.

Aljamerbaröm-Turöm: Literally meaning "town of silver" or "silver town" in Old Dwarvish, it is one of the oldest dwarven cities in existence that still stand today.

Altiri River: A winding river that flows throughout western Graecoram. It is most famously known as the place of origin of Altirtung.

Altirtung: Developed from the older Runic Form, Altirtung was named after the Altiri River in western Graecoram. It was first developed and used by a group of clerics dedicated to the study of certain holy relics. Their travels led to the language's slow spread, and the alphabet was influential in the development of Old Dwarvish, Engeltung, and many other languages in eastern Asterra.

Altris Desert: The largest desert in Xirtis and also in all of Asterra. It is home to Q'zar, the main city of the q'zardi.

A.L.Y.: The acronym for "After the Lost Years," the current age of recorded history that emerged from out of the Lost Years. This is the dating system used throughout all of Asterra. Most can determine an exact date of the end of the Lost Years based on the dating of certain ruins and objects. No one knows what happened before or during the Lost Years as almost all records were lost and only ruins and objects whose meanings have been lost to time remain. Currently, we find ourselves in the year 4124 A.L.Y.

Asterra: The great magical continent that you and I have just explored. Asterra contains over fifty realms. Its flora and fauna are as diverse as its people, languages, currencies, and traditions. Asterra is surrounded by the four great oceans: the Sillian Ocean to the east; the Nebur Ocean to the south; the Nelmin Tor Ocean to the west; and the Ars Empers Ocean to the north.

Aurora: Known as the land of farmers, Aurora is an agrarian realm located in the northeast region of the continent. It borders Ohraerandi to the south, Eurus to the northwest, and Dwathrin to the southwest. It is considered one of the main human realms within Asterra.

Ayramar: A small elvish village known for its production of mysterious goods.

Azuren Rel: Also known as the blue rose of Magris, Azuren Rel is a slang version of the Centris name for the flower, which grows most prominently throughout Magris.

Balgra: A beautiful, sprawling garden city that is the capital of the realm of Verdel. Balgra acts as a major trading hub for merchants from the western and central realms of Asterra.

Balri: The financial capital and second largest city in Magris behind Fjalth. Located in the northeast of Magris, Balri's population is almost entirely human, which is a result of the tensions that still exist between most esterelians and mid-realm humans after the War of the Sundering Steppes.

Battle of Drut Oil Fields: The final battle in the dwarven campaign to reclaim Dwathrin, which resulted in a decisive dwarven and varenijar victory and expelled the hjaeti and northern peoples from Dwathrin in 2018 A.L.Y.

Berdribrul: Former mayor of Umbris in Emberdell and friend to Sindil, Tüvlin, Elpern, and Alzamos.

Berry Bright Bale: Wonderfully delicious berry bushes found in the deep forests of Asterra.

Bridle Bristle Twine: A vicious plant/weed that can grow a multitude of long stalk-like vines, which can each measure over thirty meters long. This weed feeds off unsuspecting prey that just so happen to wander into its vicinity. All of the vines are connected to a central bulbous aperture that serves as the means of consumption of its various prey. Its presence is often accompanied by a rotting smell produced by the release of various gases from the consumption of organic matter.

Cabel: The main financial hub of Xirtis, and the home to the largest currency exchange in all of Asterra.

Caerulus River: One of the largest rivers in Asterra, which forms at the Executor Mountains in northern Ohraerandi and runs through Aurora all the way down to the southern rainforests.

Cammas Clock Tower: Located within the city of Zeris, it is known as one of the wonders of Asterra. The tower is well over a thousand years old, and though not originally designed as a clock tower, it underwent a conversion many years after its initial construction.

Carden Cottages: A small village located near Parson's Fold in Middrit.

Carlington: Located in Eurus, it is a quaint seaside town that overlooks the Sillian Ocean.

Centris: One of the most frequently spoken languages among denizens of the central realms, Centris is a derivative language of Altirtung that also borrows elements from the older and newer Runic Forms.

Compass Mountains: A great mountain range that runs through Ohraerandi and nearly divides the realm into a western and an eastern half.

Cyrix Root: A very common additive to tea in the northern and central realms, it is also widely used among the fairies thanks to Julia.

Dæmar: Son of Fürfir and Helwig who was kidnapped and brought to the underworld by Gülmirn.

Daemon: One of the three mathris who delve into the mysteries and powers of the aphotic and are manipulators of voodoo. There are several cults around the continent that worship deities of old that were known to be the leaders and rulers of certain daemons.

Danemere Færgut: Current king of the dwarven realm. His strong advocacy for dwarven industry and manufacturing has led to monumental increases in quality and efficiency, allowing for an increasingly high demand for dwarven goods despite their steep price.

Delphus: One of the main cities of the dryads within Trisden.

Del' San Cove: An eastern realm that borders the great Sillian Ocean and is located to the southeast of Eurus. Del' San Cove has had a long history of pirate and thief rule. Recent efforts by the Templar Order have lessened the grip of piracy in the north, but it is still prevalent in the south.

Djienji: One of the three mathris who are conjurers of the runic and mystics of alchemy. They usually do not interfere with human matters and are quite apathetic to that which does not pertain to their mission. However, some are known to be empathetic, and others are known to be mischievous and malicious.[21]

Dwathrin: The chief realm of the dwarves, and home to the capital of the dwarven empire, Héahfæsten. It is located in northeast Asterra, and it borders Ohraerandi to the east, Aurora to the northeast, Mikill Fjörðr to the west, Kuzengard to the south, and the Plains of Hildred to the northwest.

East Bogswurd: One of the major goblin cities located within Trisden.

Ebrillian Ore: A reddish ore found in the southern central parts of Asterra, which was the catalyst behind the War of the Sundering Steppes in 4044 A.L.Y. It is known for having many fire-like properties that make it ideal for both weapons and magic instruments.

Ei' Del River: One of the longest rivers in Asterra; it starts in the great north and runs through Dwathrin and down through Aurora before feeding into the Sillian Ocean at Del' San Cove.

Elrime Orcs: A large tribe of orcs that inhabit the northern reaches and northern lands of Asterra. They, along with the hjaeti, are sworn enemies of the dwarven people and their allies.

Elther: One of the three mathris who are spirits of the forest and conjurers of sylvan magic. They are known to be mostly benevolent, but some elther can be aggressive.

Emberdell: The largest realm that is considered within the elvish sphere of influence. It is home to many sacred groves and magical woods.

Emervell: A busy trading town located in northern Middrit, known for being one of the financial hubs of the realm. It was sieged for nigh two years by the Trifex Alliance during the War of the Sundering Steppes.

Empire of Ludus Fen: Founded by Ludus Caerolum, Ludus Fen was a great human empire of old situated west of the Caerulus River.

After helping the dwarven crown defeat the elrime orcs, the Empire of Ludus Fen was renamed to Ohraerandi in honor of the spirit of the human, dwarven, varenijar, and gnomish alliance.

Empyrean Magic: One of the seven branches of magic, the others being runic, sylvan, aphotic, elemental, alchemy, and voodoo. Empyrean magic is most commonly associated with the Templar Order, whose knights are the most prolific users in this field of magic.

Engeltung: The most widely spoken language in all of Asterra, especially within the realms of man.

Ephesian Range: A treacherous mountain range located in Verdel, which is nigh impassable through conventional means.

Esterelians: Known as "humans of the southern steppes" by many, they share just as many qualities with dragons as they do with humans. They are large in stature and have broad shoulders and long necks. They are covered in a scale-like hide similar to that of dragons, yet all of their other aspects are humanlike. They mostly live among the fiery plains of Torbar-El.

Eurus: A calm and quaint realm that is home to beautiful seaside towns and spanning coastlines as well as rustic castles and deep woods. Eurus is located to the northwest of Del' San Cove, and it borders Aurora to the southeast.

Euyril River: The second largest river in the continent, which feeds into the Nebur Ocean.

Faeril: The capital city of the nuffi within the realm of Trisden.

Fairdew Forest: The main forest of the nymphs of Trisden.

Faerstfell Chasm: A deep, gaping gorge that lies along the northernmost portion of the border between Ohraerandi and Dwathrin. It is said that the great horned beast Fülwig created the chasm with a single swipe of his great paws.

Fairy Floral: The main currency found within the fairy realms of the world, though a decent portion of gnomes have adopted the use of gild. The exchange rate for the fairy floral is 1 to 0.8 gild; thus, 15 fairy florals is equal to about 12 gild. Fairy florals also come in 0.5 and 0.25 floral coins.

F.F.A.T.: The acronym for the Fantastical Fairy Association of Trisden, which comprises the six major fairy groups within Trisden, with the exception of the nuffi until their acceptance in 4121 A.L.Y. Its current elected leader is Persax the gnome.

Fire Islands: The largest grouping of islands located off of the eastern coast of Asterra in the Sillian Ocean. The Fire Islands are known for having some of the largest ship ports within Asterra.

Forest of Grent: A deep dark wood located near Stahlt in the realm of Trisden. Many souls have gone missing in the forest, especially those of the young, which leads many to believe the forest is cursed.

Fülwig: The great horned beast and one of the guards of the underworld. Fülwig is described as standing over fifty meters tall and having bright green, poisoned eyes and a large mouth filled with horn-like teeth. His six great paws are said to have created the Faerstfell Chasm with a single swipe.

Fürfir: The chief deity of the dwarven mythos, and the first born from a divine spark within the Forge of Dæmar. Fürfir was said to have created the world after the loss of his son, Dæmar, as a task from his wife Helwig. Fürfir is the patron deity of blacksmiths, kings, and warriors.

Furifveng: A great and vile dragon that terrorized the dwarven realm during the Shattered Years before being slain by Svensson Burbeard.

Galka: The common currency used among most orc tribes. It also has become a secondary currency for goblins and has found its way into some realms of man. However, poor debt management in orcish realms due to orcs killing their creditors has decreased the value of the galka. The exchange rate is 1 galka to 0.42 gild.

Gild: The most popular currency used within Asterra, and the currency which is most common within the realms of man. Gild is broken down into other denominations of coin, with 1 gild being made up of 5 argentī, and 1 argentī being made up of 4 pieces of copper. Gild is the standard to which all other currencies are measured up against.

Glen Hollow: A quiet and wealthy village hidden within the woods of Emberdell, which contains a very large population of elvish elites.

Graecoram: An eastern realm of man that was the site of the first developments of Altirtung and also home to the Empire of Graecoram.

Grand Admiral Diana Harper: A skilled templar admiral who has been put in charge of ridding the coasts of Del' San Cove of the presence of pirates. She is known as being one of the youngest templar grand admirals in the order in recent years, and it is said she would be one of the first considerations for the rank of royal grand admiral.

Gülmirn: The second born out of the Forge of Dæmar, and the god of death. Out of envy, Gülmirn kidnapped Fürfir and Helwig's son, Dæmar, and brought him to the underworld.

Héahfæsten: Named after the first king of the dwarves, Ruffil Héahart. Héahfæsten served as the capital for the first five dwarven dynasties, and it is the current capital of the dwarven realm.

Helwig: The third born out of the Forge of Dæmar. Wife of Fürfir, she is the epitome of compassion and understanding. Helwig is the patron deity of mothers and entrepreneurs.

Hildur: A small human trading town within Trisden, which has grown popular with nuffi merchants over recent years.

Hinderlands: The wooded northern region of Dwathrin, which the dwarven crown holds a tenuous grasp of due to the woods being home to many enemies of the dwarves.

Hjaeti: A warring tribe of the northern reaches of Asterra. They are sworn enemies of the dwarves and have engaged in many conflicts over territory contained within the dwarven realm.

Holy Relics: One of three types of artifacts found throughout Asterra. Holy relics are known as being the purest among the three artifacts, and they are often the rarest and hardest to find.

Ice Troll: Surprisingly smart creatures who have an innate penchant for telling riddles and rhymes. They love to eat the boots of travelers and steal food and money from lone wanderers. They can be violent if provoked, but they are much less violent than the quick-tempered stone trolls. However, it is advised to still tread with caution when encountering an ice troll.

Idyll Sea: A beautiful, majestic sea situated off the coasts of Xirtis.

Illian Pelinar: The patron saint of Verdel who was born in Prescus in the year 3943 A.L.Y. She was known as a guardian for the lost and weary and acted as a devoted leader to many souls located within the central realms.

Inverted Cathedral: A mysterious cathedral located in Thune that is dug deep into the earth. Each of its many layers lies farther from the surface. It is said that many ritualistic sacrifices were performed here in the past as part of occult worship.

Ironbeak Hills: A small town located in Middrit that is known for many popular fables throughout Asterra.

Kuzengard: A small realm located just north of Dwathrin that is a part of the dwarven crown.

Legio Atlatica: Led by legatus legionis[22] Quintus Amaris, Legio Atlatica was a veteran legion deployed to the central realms during the War of the Sundering Steppes. It saw extensive action in the realm of Verdel during the war and was responsible for the relief of Prescus.

Little Mellow Meadow: The main town for the leprechauns of Trisden.

Lucre Moremy: A cruel, mysterious being who runs a cult within the Ochre Halls.

Luminous Grove: A majestic grove located within the Aurelian Fields of northern Aurora. The grove contains a myriad of iridescent flora, which attracts many visitors.

Lumna: The main currency used in the elvish realms. It has seen an increase in its value due to a slight increase in interest rates in the elvish realms. The exchange rate is 1 lumna equal to 1.19 gild.

Magris: A central realm that borders Middrit to the southeast and Thune to the southwest and also borders the southern portion of Verdel. It is known to have a large esterelian population in the south, a large human population in the northeast, and a small diasporic orc population in the west.

Marshes of Meldaya: Located within central Thune, these marshes were formed from the drainage of many waterways into the earth. In the mythos of Thune, it is believed that the wolf Nersir, consumer of Ädulm, lives within the Marshes of Meldaya, growing his cult to fight against the other deities of the lands and all those who follow them.

Mathris: Ancient mythical beings that, along with dragons, know the most of what the world might have been like before the Lost Years. Their stories, only oral, go back just as far as that of the dragons. They are ethereal beings, requiring little to live, but their energy is called back to the world when their missions or tasks have been fulfilled. It is said that their missions come from higher powers of old, yet even they do not know who calls them into action. Some mathris are evil, some are good, and some are apathetic to the world around them. The three mathris are djienji, daemons, and elther.

Melrin: A humanlike bipedal rodent that is commonly found within the midwestern and western realms of Asterra.

Middrit: A central realm that is northwest of Magris and borders Thune to the west, Verdel to the east, and Saires to the south.

Mikill Fjörðr: The second largest realm contained within the dwarven sphere of influence and a part of the dwarven crown. Its many fjords are home to the greatest population of varenijar in all of Asterra.

Mirist Lake: The largest lake in all of Saires, which is home to a secluded island that contains many wondrous treasures.

Mirþris-Dún: The far northeastern portion of Dwathrin, which lies to the east of the Hinderlands and borders the northwest portion of Mikill Fjörðr.

Misty Flower Woods: The main hideaway for the cluricauns of Trisden.

Norman's Point: The southern tip of the Sarcino Coast in Del' San Cove.

Nuffi: Often referred to as the (unofficial) "seventh class of fairies" or as the "impure fairies," nuffi are a mixture of the bloodlines of fairies (mostly dryads and nymphs), humans, and sometimes elves. For these reasons, they usually possess traits of all three races. They are often quite larger than "normal" fairies and mostly live isolated from other fairies within the central plains and northern woods of Asterra. However, since the F.F.A.T.'s decree to include them in their meetings in 4121 A.L.Y., most fairies and fairy realms consider nuffi official fairies. However, not all realms have adopted this ruling, leading the distinction to still be made between nuffi and other fairies.

Oak Rose Wine: A very fancy type of red wine that is often produced in the western and central regions of Asterra.

Old Dwarvish: Formed almost three thousand years ago, Old Dwarvish was the chief language of the dwarven people and their realm and, in those times, was simply called Dwarvish. Though the most spoken language in the dwarven realm today is Engeltung, Old Dwarvish can still be heard and seen throughout all dwarven lands. Its alphabet contains thirty characters and twenty-five letters and was inspired by Altirtung and the older Runic Form.

Old Dwarvish Alphabet

a, ꙮ, Ꝇ, d, e, ĕ, ꙍ, ꙓ, h, i, ꚃ, ꚅ, j, l, m, n, ꞑ, **o**, ö, Ᵽ, **r**, s, t, þ, u, ü, v, w, Ꙡ, y

- ❖ For the vowels a and e, Old Dwarvish utilizes an upside down ᴧ mark on top of the vowel to distinguish between long a and short a and long e and short e.
- ❖ Ꝇ is pronounced like the Bj in *Björn*.
- ❖ ꙍ is pronounced *eft*.
- ❖ ꙓ is pronounced *gelt* and is known as the gale symbol.
- ❖ ꚃ is pronounced like the word *eye*.
- ❖ ꚅ is pronounced *eeya*.
- ❖ ꞑ is pronounced *rn* where the r is slightly rolled and both letters are pronounced. The sound produced by the letter ꞑ is slightly different sounding than when the letters rn are together in words such as arno = iron.
- ❖ Ᵽ is pronounced the same way as the letter p in Engeltung.
- ❖ Ꙡ is pronounced *kruw* or like a harsh pronunciation of the word *crew*, and it is known as the crow symbol.
- ❖ Umlauts are pronounced similarly to the long ō or ū in Altirtung, but there is a slight roll as if a soft e were at the end.
- ❖ J is short like in *jarl* and is most often used and found before the vowels a, e, o, u, and the letter ꙍ.
- ❖ The letter Y is rare, but it is often used before stressed vowels, the vowel i, special characters, and before the letter j.

Oxish: A term used to describe an investor who is optimistic about the growing strength of a financial instrument, security, or commodity.

Paldermen: A deity of the old times, and one of the leaders of daemons. He is known as a devourer of the light in order to help him restore his fiendish gaze.

Parson's Fold: A small town located in Middrit that was founded after the War of the Sundering Steppes to provide a safe haven for the weary to seek refuge from the terrors of the world. However, the true intent of its founding was veiled from most denizens.

Pelthom: From the Old Dwarvish word for "money," the pelthom is commonly used in the realms of the dwarves, hjaeti, and even gnomes. In fact, it is the second most used currency for gnomes after the fairy floral. The pelthom is also the second most used currency in Asterra as it has also enjoyed popularity among esterelian traders in the southern parts of the continent. This has been due to a steady increase in the demand for dwarven goods under King Danemere. The exchange rate is 1 pelthom equal to 1.8 gild.

Pilas Cane: A very rare sweet cane found only in the southern central realms. It is sometimes used as an alternative to sugar in cooking and baking. However, due to its rarity, it is seldom used and can be very expensive. The maceration and fermentation of pilas cane is used in the production of pillacella liquor.

Pilder Puff Fish: A rare fish used in making pilder puff stew.

Pilder Puff Stew: A hearty stew made with the rare pilder puff fish. It is a staple dish among the eastern coastal realms of Asterra.

Pillacella: A very rare type of liquor that is created from the maceration and fermentation of pilas cane. It is a sweet after-dinner liquor and quite rare and expensive.

Plains of Hildred: The southernmost realm contained within the dwarven sphere of influence and a part of the dwarven crown. It is located south of Mikill Fjörðr.

Prescus: A great city carved within the Ephesian Mountain Range. It offers safe passage through the treacherous mountains into the western portion of Verdel near the capital of Balgra. Prescus was home to the patron saint of Verdel, Illian Pelinar.

Q'zardi: The ancient inhabitants of the southern and central deserts of the continent, who are skilled in the art of jewel crafting, embroidery, and pneumatics. They are only a little taller than gnomes, but they are built more like elves. They have thick olive-colored fur and large pointy ears. The older and newer Runic Form are still loosely used by some of the q'zardi.

Regjar Root: A rare plant found within the mountainous regions of the central and northern lands of Asterra. It is a rare plant, and its medicinal qualities make it highly sought by apothecaries. It also has a special use for various anointing practices of kings and queens in the central realms, especially by the druids in Thune. It is often guarded by ice trolls, who view the plant as sacred to their lands.

Reider: Fürfir's greatest chieftain, who was entrusted with guarding the world from Gülmirn and his agents of evil.

Rezsev: A town located on the coast of southern Eurus near the border of Del' San Cove. It is known for having the best pilder puff stew on the entire northeast coast of Asterra.

Ruby-Stone Shrooms: Considered a delicacy for baking and cooking, they are usually found in very dark caves and groves all over Asterra.

Ruffil Héahart: The first king of the dwarves, who united the dwarves and varenijar and successfully retook Dwathrin from the hjaeti tribes and other northern peoples. The city of Héahfæsten was founded in his honor, and his rule started the dwarven imperial period, of which the first five dynasties are referred to as the amaranthine age.

Runes: One of the three types of artifacts found throughout Asterra, the other two being true-forged weapons and holy relics, runes are known as being the most enchanted out of the three, and their use is highly restricted by the dwarves.

Runic Form: Also known by some as Runic Vocul, Runic Form was one of the first languages to develop from the ancient hieroglyphs found among the scattered ruins in the deserts of Xirtis. The older version of Runic Form was influential in the development of many languages throughout Asterra, such as Altirtung and Old Dwarvish. While the older version of Runic Form is still used today, a newer version is more popular among those who choose to converse in the language.

Saires: A central realm located to the northwest of Thune. It is known for its collection of large lakes, of which Mirist Lake is the largest.

Sairien Owl: An extremely intellectual species of owl that is able to converse in many different forms of speech. They are quite rare as they tend to do their best to avoid humans and other similar beings in Asterra. However, if one were to try to find them, the best place would be in the realm of Saires.

Sarcino Coast: The northern most coastline of Del' San Cove, which is home to the Sunken Gardens, Port Town, Elgith, Cedar Side Cottages, and Norman's Point.

Shattered Years: The period following the dwarven imperial age in which the dwarven realm was split into six warring city-states.

Solemn Vow Abbey: A small abbey dedicated to the light that is located in Ohraerandi. Its clerics study the empyrean and are dedicated to spreading peace.

Stahlt: A rustic town located in central Trisden.

Stelford: One of the main gnomish cities located within Trisden.

Stonefel Pass: A long and arduous hiking trail located in northern Emberdell that is only for the most daring of adventurers.

Stone Trolls: One of the three common types of trolls that are found throughout Asterra. They are quick-tempered and often far more vicious than ice trolls or woodland trolls and are also the largest of the three.

Svensson Burbeard: The great dwarven hero of old, who was born of both dwarven and varenijar stock. He is known as the vanquisher of the dragon Furifveng and the evil necromancer Vulmor, and he reunited the six city-states, ending the period of the Shattered Years. He was slain by an assassin loyal to the hjaeti tribes. Svensson is still celebrated today as one of the greatest heroes in dwarven history.

Templar Order: The holy vanguards of Asterra, and the keepers of records and stewards of artifacts. They are devoted to the empyrean and are the most prolific users of empyrean incantations throughout all of Asterra. Their order was founded over two millennia ago in the fifteenth century A.L.Y., and their main citadel, Aeternitus, is located in northern Ohraerandi. Their traditions imbue majesty not only in their sacrosanct buildings and meetings but also in their machinery and communication, of which they forgo gunpowder to emblazon their armaments with empyrean sparks. They converse in Altirtung to bewilder their foes and bestow honor upon certain matters.

Tide Shifter: The pirate captain Algreven Lockjaw's famed true-forged sword, which has control over the tides: the sharp edge of its blade can cut through and toss water, while its dull edge draws water like a magnet.

Torbar-El: A fiery and fierce southern-central realm that is the primary home of the esterelians. Torbar-El's rocky landscape is a mix of active and dormant volcanoes, perilous mountain ranges, charred earth, patches of dense tropical fauna, arid and desolate deserts, and sprawling iron and stone cities.

Trifex Alliance: An alliance of esterelians, orcs, and humans that started the War of the Sundering Steppes in 4044 A.L.Y. The war raged for seven years until the Trifex Alliance was defeated by a coalition of the Templar Order and sovereign central realms.

Trisden: A northern realm located to the west of Ohraerandi, it is primarily inhabited by humans but maintains a decently sized fairy population.

True-Forged Weapons: Known as being the most enhanced among the three artifacts, true-forged weapons possess incalculable power and are each imbued with unique characteristics.

Turi: The great huntress and one of the guards of the underworld.

Varenijar: The tall and strong kin of the dwarves, they live alongside dwarves in the northern realms. However, unlike the dwarves who sought refuge in the mountains and mines of Dwathrin, the varenijar found their peace on the shores of the sea. Their main strongholds lie in the great fjords of Mikill Fjörðr. They are great fighters and are very loyal, and they have a penchant for dwarven weapons.

Verdant Heart Flower: A flower that grows so green that its center shines magnificently bright with an alluring luminous glow. It is used for potions that mend the wounds of the heart. It is sometimes called the light of winter for its ability to ease the enveloping darkness of sadness in its patients. The flower is found in many northern and northeast territories but most notably in Dwathrin and Ohraerandi.

Verdel: A central realm that is located to the west of Middrit and borders Tenai to the east and Natusaka to the north.

Verza: An ancient town nestled in the laurel hills of southern Graecoram.

Vulmor: An evil necromancer who attempted to harness the power of a dwarven rune to control nature before being slain by Svensson Burbeard.

War of the Sundering Steppes: A devastating conflict that started in 4044 A.L.Y. over a territorial dispute pertaining to the Tor' Nezun Mountains, which separate southeastern Verdel, southwestern Magris, and northern Torbar-El. The esterelians, along with several groups of orcs and men, wished to seize most of the mountains' rich supply of ebrillian ore. The conflict spanned seven years and involved many realms throughout Asterra.

Wilder Woods: A dense, somewhat peaceful forest located in Emberdell.

Windyrose River: The longest river in Emberdell.

Windy Walnut Way: A large ogre town located within Trisden.

Wolfish: Used to describe an investor who is pessimistic about the performance of a financial instrument, security, or commodity.

Woodland Trolls: The smallest of the three common types of trolls, they are still known to be extremely mischievous. They are not as vicious as the stone trolls or as clever as the ice trolls, but they find ways to harass travelers. Some love riddles and rhymes like ice trolls, but most aren't witty enough to play along (but there are always exceptions).

Xirtis: The largest realm in all of Asterra, which is made up of sprawling deserts, ancient ruins, and lush oases. Xirtis contains the largest population of q'zardi in all of Asterra and is home to the largest currency exchange and oldest library in Asterra. It is located in southwest Asterra.

Xirtis Currency Exchange: The largest currency exchange in all of Asterra, which is located in Cabel.

Zeris: A great trading hub that is located on Al' Fer's Bay and is home to the great Cammas Clock Tower.

ENDNOTES

1   Cluricauns are creatures of Irish folklore. They aren't referenced as much in literary sources, which might be indicative of their subtle and mischievous nature.

2   I based the name *varenijar* off the term *Varangian* used by the Byzantines for Norsemen who fought for the emperor and the Byzantine Empire during the Middle Ages. The word stems from the Old Icelandic word *Væringjar*, meaning "men of the pledge" (*Viking Language 1*, 171–2).

3   The name *hjaeti* was inspired by the helvetii tribe, who were one of the catalysts for the start of the Gallic Wars. The hjaeti are much different, though, than the historical helvetii.

4   The influence for this tale is the creation myths of Old Norse and Greek Mythology.

5   The creation of Old Dwarvish was inspired by mixing a bit of the grammar and vocabulary of Old Icelandic, Latin, and English.

6   The name *Ohraerandi* was created from an amalgamation of Old Icelandic words.

7   The story of Svensson is loosely inspired by the story of Sigurd in the *Saga of Volsungs*.

8   The name *Gælahud Færgut* is partially inspired by Launcelot's son in *Le' Morte De Arthur* by Sir Thomas Malory.

9   I was inspired after discovering the quote by Admiral Sir Andrew Cunningham in Bevin Alexander's book *How Hitler Could Have Won World War II*. To quote: "It takes the navy three years to build a ship, but three hundred years to build a tradition; we must not let the army down" (69).

10 The language of the Templar Order is Latin, which is called Altirtung in Asterra.

11 "Greek fire" used by the Byzantine and Eastern Roman Empire

was a precursor to napalm and was devastating against ships during the Middle Ages.

12 The effects of interest rates upon the currency of Asterra was researched through *Investopedia*.

13 The effects of debt upon the currency of Asterra was researched through *Investopedia*.

14 Information on the peregrine falcon was obtained through *Wikipedia*.

15 Basics of currency trading was researched in *Currency Trading for Dummies* and *Investopedia*.

16 Investment instruments for the currency market were gathered from *Currency Trading for Dummies*.

17 Investment strategies for the currency market were gathered from *Currency Trading for Dummies*.

18 For the looks of the q'zardi I was inspired a bit by the appearance of the fennec fox.

19 This Latin poem is in the form of twelve hexameters. I learned how to write Latin poetry by reading *Beginning Latin Poetry*. I was greatly inspired by the works of Ovid, Vergil, and Horace. For this poem I took some liberties in order to make the meters work (e.g., I used meī instead of meus, a, um for metrical convenience, and I also made dies, which is a feminine/masculine noun, feminine here for convenience).

20 The four pillars/essentials of magic are inspired by the esoteric studies into alchemy throughout history and basic principles of physics.

21 The name *djienji* was inspired by the name of the jinni in *The Arabian Nights*.

22 The Templar Order's military is loosely inspired by the Roman Army, with some of the titles being bestowed upon commanders having the same name and designation.

Bibliography/Inspirations

Alexander, Bevin. *How Hitler Could Have Won World War II: The Fatal Errors That Led to Nazi Defeat.* New York: Three Rivers Press, 2000.

Banton, Caroline. "What is a Currency Peg?" *Investopedia*, updated April 3, 2021, https://www.investopedia.com/terms/c/currency-peg.asp#:~:text=A%20currency%20peg%20is%20a,exchange%20rates%20for%20business%20planning.

Barthram, Phil. "Old English to Modern English Translator." *Old English Translator*, https://www.oldenglishtranslator.co.uk/. Accessed 2016–2021.

Betts, Gavin, and Daniel Franklin. *Beginning Latin Poetry Reader: 70 Selections from the Great Periods of Roman Verse and Drama.* New York: McGraw-Hill, 2007.

Betts, Gavin, and Daniel Franklin. *The Big Gold Book of Latin Verbs: 555 Verbs Fully Conjugated.* New York: McGraw-Hill, 2004.

Bradbury, Ray. *Something Wicked This Way Comes.* 1962. London: Folio Society, 2019.

Brooks, Kathleen and Brian Dolan. *Currency Trading for Dummies.* 3rd ed. Hoboken: John Wiley & Sons, 2015.

Burton, Sir Richard Francis, translator. *The Arabian Nights.* New York: Barnes & Noble, 2016.

Byock, Jesse L. *Viking Language 1: Learn Old Norse, Runes, and Icelandic Sagas.* Pacific Palisades: Jules William Press, 2013.

Caesar, Gaius Julius. *The Gallic War.* Translated by H. J. Edwards. Cambridge, MA: Harvard University Press, 1917.

Chen, James. "What is Currency Appreciation?" *Investopedia*, updated March 22, 2021. https://www.investopedia.com/terms/c/currency-appreciation.asp#:~:text=Currency%20appreciation%20is%20an%20increase,trade%20balances%2C%20and%20business%20cycles.

Crofton, T. Croker. "Seeing is Believing." In *A Treasury of Irish Fairy and Folk Tales*, compiled by Crofton, 190-92. New York: Sterling Publishing, 2015.

Crofton, T. Croker. "The Haunted Cellar." In *A Treasury of Irish Fairy and Folk Tales*, compiled by Crofton, 197-202. New York: Sterling Publishing, 2016.

"Fennec Fox." *Wikipedia*, updated August 1st, 2022. https://en.wikipedia.org/wiki/Fennec_fox.

"First Law of Thermodynamics." *Wikipedia*, updated August 24th, 2022.https://en.wikipedia.org/wiki/First_law_of_thermodynamics.

"Fundamental Interaction." *Wikipedia*, updated August 2nd, 2022. https://en.wikipedia.org/wiki/Fundamental_interaction.

Garrett, Jack. "The Vikings of Bjornstad: Life in the Age of the Vikings, Normans and Anglo Saxons." *The Vikings of Bjornstad*, https://www.vikingsofbjornstad.com/index.htm. Accessed 2016–2018.

Goldsworthy, Adrian Keith. *The Complete Roman Army*. London: Thames & Hudson, 2008.

"Greek Fire." *Wikipedia*, updated March 10, 2022, https://en.wikipedia.org/wiki/Greek_fire.

Guerber, Helen A. *Tales of Norse Mythology*. New York: Sterling Publishing, 2017.

Kuhn, F. Karl and Frank Noschese. *Basic Physics: A Self Teaching Guide*. 3rd ed. Hoboken: Jossey-Bass, 2020.

"Laurus Nobilis." *Wikipedia*, updated May 24, 2022, https://en.wikipedia.org/wiki/Laurus_nobilis.

Lioudis, Nick. "How National Interest Rates Affect Currency Values and Exchange Rates." *Investopedia*, updated September 30, 2021. https://www.investopedia.com/ask/answers/040315/how-do-changes-national-interest-rates-affect-currencys-value-and-exchange-rate.asp#:~:text=Generally%2C%20higher%20interest%20rates%20increase,of%20the%20home%20country's%20currency.

Littlejohn, Joyce, et al. *Collins Latin Concise Dictionary*. New York: HarperCollins, 2003.

Malory, Thomas. *Le Morte d' Arthur: King Arthur and the Knights of* the Round Table. New York: Barnes and Noble, 2015.

"Peregrine Falcon." Wikipedia, updated March 15, 2022. https://en.wikipedia.org/wiki/Peregrine_falcon.

Roob, Alexander. Alchemy & Mysticism. Cologne: Benedikt Taschen Verlag, 1997.

The Saga of the Volsungs: The Norse Epic of Sigurd the Dragon Slayer. Translated and edited by Jesse Byock. London: Penguin Classics, 1999.

Tolkien, J. R. R. The Annotated Hobbit. London: Allen, 1937. Boston: Houghton Mifflin Company, n.d.

Tolkien, J. R. R. The Lord of The Rings. London: Allen, 1954–1955. Boston: Houghton Mifflin Company, n.d.

Twin, Alexandra. "6 Factors That Influence Exchange Rates." Investopedia, updated June 8, 2021, https://www.investopedia.com/trading/factors-influence-exchange-rates/.

Wilde, Oscar. The Selfish Giant and Other Stories. London: Folio Society, 2013.

Acknowledgments

This collection would have never taken appropriate form if it weren't for the following, who all have my eternal gratitude and thanks for documenting and sharing their stories and knowledge of the events contained within this collection.

To the people of Zeris, who have kept the story of Haza Izmir alive over the passing centuries. "Captured Time," 2856 A.L.Y.

To Julia Sable and her wondrous adventurous spirit, and to her family. "Julia's Great Adventure," 4121 A.L.Y.

To the people of Carlington and especially to folklorist Brimel Wildun, for his recordings of the events of Carlington. "The Marker of Tides," 4097 A.L.Y.

To the dwarven historian Brindabar Baldil, for sharing his expert analysis on the dwarven people and their history. "A Study on the Dwarves," 4114 A.L.Y.

In honor of the countless reports made near the Ochre Halls of those trapped within. "Candles of the Ochre Halls," 4118 A.L.Y.

To Hiro Ichigura and the rest of the noble defenders of Prescus, and to Quintus Amaris and Legio Atlatica for the relief of Prescus and the recovery of Hiro's journal. "The Fires of Prescus," 4045 A.L.Y.

To the good and brave souls who fled Parson's Fold and bravely told their story. "The Cult of Paldermen," 4071 A.L.Y.

To Antonio Avalano and his family. "Upon Laurel Roads," 4096 A.L.Y.

To the memory of Mr. Thims, whose journal kept the story and soul of Henry Stillton alive. "A Trial of Thieves," 4109 A.L.Y.

To Medriel Varlin, famed adventurer and holder of the aquamarine heart of the noble serpent. "An Aquamarine Heart," 4052 A.L.Y.

To Rodolfo Illia and Salerina Valdiza and their most favorable camaraderie in the darkest of times. "The Secret of Norman's Point,"

4119 A.L.Y.

To Lester Mann and his indomitable spirit, and to Abigail Halsen who has shared his story. "Lester Mann and the Hollow Hearth," 4110 A.L.Y.

To the *Cabel Chronicle*, and to Grimaldo Elwidget. "Currency Investing with Grimaldo Elwidget," 4122 A.L.Y.

For the friendly journey and dedication of Tüvlin Dundern, Alzamos Ixsil, Elpern Orn' Tor, and Sindil Syillis. "Four for Pillacella," 4122 A.L.Y.

For the original version of the "Adventurer's Hymn," written before the reformation of Altirtung by the templar and their adoption of it as their oath of acceptance to the weary. "A Templar's Hymn," originally dated from the fifteenth century A.L.Y.

About the Author

Photo by Maggie McGill Photography

Michael Rizzo is a thirty-year-old fantasy fiction writer, who works in finance during the day and often spends evenings writing and creating his fantasy world. When not exploring Asterra, he enjoys indulging his love for adventure with family trips throughout Europe, the Mediterranean, and the Caribbean. In his spare time, he also enjoys hanging out with his dogs and playing guitar in his band.

Made in the USA
Middletown, DE
05 May 2024

53864060R00117